Introduction to

MOLECULAR-ORBITAL THEORY

Introduction to

MOLECULAR-ORBITAL THEORY

Arno Liberles

FAIRLEIGH DICKINSON UNIVERSITY

TEANECK, NEW JERSEY

HOLT, RINEHART AND WINSTON, INC.

New York • Chicago • San Francisco • Toronto • London

TO ELLEN

PREFACE

During the past few years, several texts that deal with the subject of molecular-orbital theory have appeared. For the most part, these are books on quantum chemistry, which cover quantum mechanics in a thorough and rigorous manner and devote one or more chapters to molecular-orbital theory. These texts are designed for the reader who has a good knowledge of mathematics and physics; they are intended for use in a graduate course on quantum mechanics. There are, in addition, several excellent books designed primarily for organic chemists. These books are also intended for graduate level courses in which prior knowledge of modern physics and wave mechanics is assumed. With the ever increasing use of the concepts of molecular-orbital theory to explain the structure of molecules, it seems desirable to introduce this subject at an earlier stage.

The present text is intended for an introductory course in molecular-orbital theory and no prior knowledge of either modern physics or wave mechanics is necessary. Portions of the material contained in this book have been used in conjunction with a course in theoretical organic chemistry given at Fairleigh Dickinson University. Most of the students in this course were seniors although juniors and graduate students were also enrolled. These students had no difficulty in assimilating the material.

There are many chemists who have already received their formal education and who do want some knowledge of molecular-orbital theory but who do not have the time to read extensively on the subject. It is possible that this text can be used for individual study.

When all is said and done, regardless of who may read this text, I hope that the reader finds it interesting and informative.

Thanks are due to my colleagues and students at Fairleigh Dickinson University for their encouragement during the writing of the manuscript. I am indebted to the reviewers who read the manuscript prior to its publica-

v

tion and who offered many helpful suggestions. I should also like to thank Dr. W. Arthur, Department of Physics, Fairleigh Dickinson University, and Dr. A. J. Sonnessa, Department of Chemistry, Seton Hall University for helpful discussions.

November 1965
Teaneck, New Jersey   A.L.

CONTENTS

Chapter Three

Chapter Four

Chapter Five

Chapter Six

Chapter Seven

Chapter One

CLASSICAL MECHANICS AND MODERN PHYSICS

1. INTRODUCTION

Application of the principles of quantum mechanics to the chemistry of molecules has resulted in the development of molecular-orbital theory. This theory assumes a molecule to be comprised of nuclei fixed in space. The several electrons that are then introduced one by one into the electro-static field of the nuclei travel over the entire molecule. The problem now becomes one of determining the energy levels of the electrons and picturing their orbitals. Orbitals in quantum mechanics represent regions within which the electron is likely to be found, that is, regions of high probability (high electron density).

Before discussing molecular-orbital theory in detail, let us familiarize ourselves with certain basic concepts of classical physics and then use these concepts to point out some of the observations that necessitated a revision of classical physics. This will put the subject of molecular-orbital theory into better perspective and give us some feeling for the principles involved.

2. A REVIEW OF CLASSICAL PHYSICS

Although many of the properties of atoms and molecules depend in a very definite way upon magnetic interactions, these will be neglected in all of our discussions.

We may associate with a particle of mass m, which is moving in any direction, a linear velocity v and consequently a linear momentum p.

$$p = mv \qquad (1.1)$$

Along with the linear momentum the particle may possess angular momentum L about a point O (see Figure 1–1). Let us construct a straight line connecting the particle and O. The angular momentum is then given by

$$L = mvr \qquad (1.2)$$

where r is the length of this line (the distance of the particle from O), and mv is the component of the linear momentum of the particle in the direction perpendicular to r.

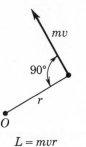

$$L = mvr$$

FIGURE 1–1   THE ANGULAR MOMENTUM
OF A PARTICLE ABOUT A POINT, O

For a particle that is moving along a circular path about O, its velocity and consequently its linear momentum, are always tangential to the circle. The angular momentum is again $L = mvr$ where r is now the radius of the circle (see Figure 1–2).

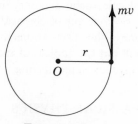

FIGURE 1–2

According to Newton's second law of mechanics, *a force gives rise to a change in the linear momentum with time.*

$$F = \frac{d(mv)}{dt}$$

or

$$F = \frac{dp}{dt} \qquad (1.3)$$

where t is the time. If the mass m is constant,

$$F = m\frac{dv}{dt}$$

then

$$F = ma$$

where a is the acceleration of the particle.

In addition to mechanical forces, we shall also be working with Coulombic forces. The force between two charged particles is given by Coulomb's law, which states that *the force of attraction or repulsion between two charged particles is directly proportional to the product of their charges and inversely proportional to the square of the distance between them.* Coulomb's law can be expressed in mathematical form by the equation

$$F = \frac{Q_1 Q_2}{r^2} \qquad (1.4)$$

where Q_1 represents the charge of particle one, Q_2 represents the charge of particle two, and r the distance between them.

A particle also possesses total energy E

$$E = T + U$$

where T is its kinetic energy and U its potential energy.

$$T = \frac{mv^2}{2} = \frac{mv^2}{2} \cdot \frac{m}{m} = \frac{m^2v^2}{2m} = \frac{p^2}{2m} \qquad (1.5)$$

Multiplying both numerator and denominator in equation (1.5) by m, we obtain an equivalent expression for the kinetic energy in terms of the linear momentum of the particle. This expression will be of importance in connection with our quantum theory. In this discussion and all subsequent discussions, we shall assume that within a molecule the nuclei are stationary. Their kinetic energy is therefore zero. U will be the Coulombic potential energy associated with one charged particle in the electrostatic field of another. This is given by

$$U = \frac{Q_1 Q_2}{r} \qquad (1.6)$$

where Q_1 and Q_2 again represent the charge associated with each particle and r the distance separating them.

Considering the electronic charge to be $-e$ and the charge of a proton to be $+e$, requires e to be a positive number (4.8×10^{-10} statcoulomb). Notice that U is positive if both Q_1 and Q_2 are positive and also if both Q_1 and Q_2 are negative. Thus, a repulsive potential energy is positive. An attractive potential energy is negative, Q_1 positive and Q_2 negative, while a particle in the absence of an electrostatic field has $U = 0$. The potential energy between two electrons now becomes

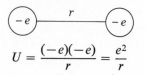

$$U = \frac{(-e)(-e)}{r} = \frac{e^2}{r}$$

while the potential energy of an electron in the field of a proton is

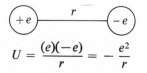

$$U = \frac{(e)(-e)}{r} = -\frac{e^2}{r}$$

A concept that plays an important role in both classical and quantum theory is that of the Hamiltonian of a system. Consider an isolated system composed of one or more particles. We shall assume that the total energy of this system remains constant, and in that case, the Hamiltonian of this system is merely its total energy, which we can write as:

$$H = E = T + U \tag{1.7}$$

where T is the total kinetic energy of the system and U the total potential energy. When working with the Hamiltonian, the kinetic energy of a particle is expressed as $p^2/2m$, not as $mv^2/2$.

For a particle that has no potential energy, $U = 0$ and equation (1.7) becomes

$$H = T = \frac{p^2}{2m} \tag{1.8}$$

For the hydrogen atom (remember that the proton is assumed to be stationary) the Hamiltonian takes the form

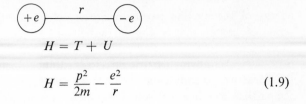

$$H = T + U$$

$$H = \frac{p^2}{2m} - \frac{e^2}{r} \tag{1.9}$$

where p is the momentum of the electron, m its mass, and r is the distance between the proton and electron.

For the helium atom

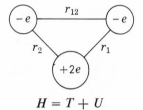

$$H = T + U$$

$$H = \frac{p_1^2}{2m} + \frac{p_2^2}{2m} - \frac{2e^2}{r_1} - \frac{2e^2}{r_2} + \frac{e^2}{r_{12}} \tag{1.10}$$

where p_1 is the momentum of electron one, p_2 is the momentum of electron two, $(-2e^2/r_1)$ represents the attraction of electron one for the nucleus, $(-2e^2/r_2)$ the attraction of electron two, and (e^2/r_{12}) the repulsion between electrons.

For the hydrogen molecule

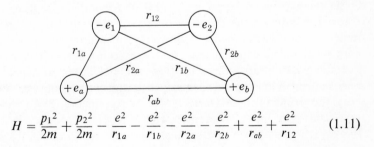

$$H = \frac{p_1^2}{2m} + \frac{p_2^2}{2m} - \frac{e^2}{r_{1a}} - \frac{e^2}{r_{1b}} - \frac{e^2}{r_{2a}} - \frac{e^2}{r_{2b}} + \frac{e^2}{r_{ab}} + \frac{e^2}{r_{12}} \tag{1.11}$$

Assume that a charged particle with kinetic energy T approaches a stationary particle of opposite charge, for example, an electron approaching a proton. The two particles are attracted, the electron moves closer to the proton, and the potential energy of the system decreases. Since the total energy of the system must remain constant, this requires that the kinetic energy of the moving particle increase. Now, for these two particles to remain together, that is, for the system of two particles to be stable, this excess kinetic energy must be lost in some manner. If the kinetic energy is not lost, the moving particle possesses enough kinetic energy to overcome the attractive potential, and it can move on. If it loses some kinetic energy, the particle no longer has sufficient kinetic energy to overcome the potential holding it, and the system is stable. Stability implies that the negative potential energy is greater in magnitude than the positive kinetic energy. Since the total energy $E = T + U$, this means that E must be negative for stable systems.

3. THE INADEQUACY OF CLASSICAL PHYSICS

Just before the turn of the century it was generally regarded that using the techniques of classical physics, the physicists of the time had answered successfully the most serious problems confronting them. Furthermore, it was generally felt that these same classical methods would serve to solve the remaining as well as future problems. Physics as a science had advanced steadily. Newton in the 1600s had formulated his laws of mechanics. These laws gave to the field of mechanics a rigor then unknown in any other area of physics. Furthermore, Newton's work was followed by that of Lagrange and Hamilton who generalized his principles, and finally, Maxwell developed laws concerning electromagnetic phenomena. These two branches of physics — classical mechanics and classical electromagnetic theory — rested upon this foundation.

In the years following these developments experiment after experiment confirmed these theories. Virtually no conflicts arose, and those occasional discrepancies between experiment and theory that did arise were ultimately removed without undue difficulty by expanding only slightly the existing framework of classical theory. However, as measuring instruments became more precise and experimental data concerning the behavior of atoms accumulated, contradictions with these theories began to appear, contradictions that could in no way be reconciled with classical physics. Simultaneously, the results of the Michelson-Morley experiment, 1887, indicated that some revision of the then-accepted laws of physics was certainly necessary. This experiment showed that light, as measured on the earth, traveled with the same velocity in all directions. In order to explain this fact Einstein found it necessary to modify Newton's laws of mechanics, and with this step he demonstrated forcefully the inadequacy of classical physics.

3.1. RELATIVITY Perhaps the best publicized concept of modern physics that is at variance with the classical picture is the theory of relativity.

Einstein set down the basic postulates of relativity in 1905; his equation,

$$E = mc^2 \tag{1.12}$$

where E is the relativistic energy of a particle, m its relativistic mass, and c the velocity of light (3×10^{10} cm/sec) has received more publicity than any other single equation. Early confirmation of the special theory of relativity came in 1909 when Bücherer showed that the e/m ratio is smaller for fast moving electrons than for slow ones. The mass of a rapidly moving electron must, therefore, be larger than the mass of a slowly moving electron. Equation (1.12) has since been substantiated by many experiments, and its validity is unquestionable.

Assuming a light wave to be composed of photons (we shall have more to say about this later) that move with velocity c,

$$c = v$$

and we define p for a photon as

$$p = mv = mc$$

we may then rewrite equation (1.12) as

$$E = mc^2 = mcc = pc \tag{1.13}$$

where p is the relativistic momentum of the photon and m its relativistic mass. Equation (1.13) is not generally correct, but it is correct for photons.

3.2. BLACK-BODY RADIATION   Another early theory that did not concur with classical physics was that used by Planck to explain *black-body* radiation. A black body is an ideal material, which absorbs all light (radiation) incident upon it. Such a substance that absorbs light of all frequencies can not be found in nature; however, a simple laboratory model that closely approximates a black body is a hollow box of opaque material with a small opening in its side as shown in Figure 1–3. All light falling upon the opening passes into the box. The opening of the box acts as a black body because all radiation incident upon it is absorbed and passes inside. The interior walls of the box absorb and emit this radiation, and eventually it passes back out through the opening.

Since the opening of the box does behave as a black body, we can determine experimentally the frequency of any emerging radiation, and this will be a good approximation to the frequency of light from an ideal

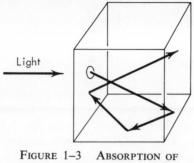

FIGURE 1–3   ABSORPTION OF
LIGHT   BY   A   BLACK   BODY

black body. Determination of the total amount of light emitted at various temperatures indicates that as the temperature increases, a black body emits more light. In addition, the average frequency, which is related to the average energy of emitted radiation, is greater, the greater the temperature. Thus, a hot black body emits not only more light but light of higher energy than a cold black body.

Using the concepts of classic physics, several investigators attempted to explain this phenomenon. All of these investigations yielded results that were incompatible with the experimental facts. The result of one such investigation predicts that the light emitted by a black body at any temperature above absolute zero will be of infinite energy. But this is impossible! This theory fails, yet it is not the investigators who are at fault here. It is the classical theory that is inadequate. One is forced to conclude that classical physics has certain limitations and that it is necessary to go beyond these limits in order to explain black-body radiation.

Planck in 1901 arrived at the formula that correctly predicts the emission of light by a black body at any temperature.[1] To solve the problem of black-body radiation, Planck first searched for an empirical equation that concurred with the experimental evidence. Having found such an equation, he next modified the classical theory so that it was in agreement with this equation. Planck's original theory dealt with the particles that made up the walls of the black body, for example, the particles making up the interior walls of a box such as the one illustrated in Figure 1–3. These particles, he assumed, were not necessarily stationary; some of them vibrated. A particle could vibrate with frequency v about an equilibrium position. This type of phenomenon is similar to the vibrations of a spring or the oscillations of a pendulum. Planck then postulated that the energy of a particle

---

[1] M. Planck, *Ann. Physik*, **4**, 553 (1901).

in the walls of this box could not have all possible values, only those values 0, $h\nu$, $2h\nu$, $3h\nu$, and so forth.

$$E = nh\nu \qquad n = 0, 1, 2, 3\cdots \qquad (1.14)$$

where h is a constant of proportionality now known as Planck's constant (6.63×10^{-27} erg-sec). Planck quantized the energy of a particle in the walls of the black body, and in this way quantum theory was born. Furthermore, this particle could only emit radiation having the same frequency with which it was vibrating, and the energy of the emitted light waves had to be proportional to the energy of the particle itself.

A more modern interpretation of Planck's work dispenses with the particle and considers only the light waves. Inside the container a light wave of frequency ν cannot assume all energy states, only those allowed by equation (1.14). We can quantize the energy of the light waves directly.

$$E = nh\nu \qquad n = 0, 1, 2, 3\cdots \qquad (1.15)$$

where E is the total energy of the wave, ν its frequency, and h Planck's constant.

3.3. PHOTOELECTRIC EFFECT

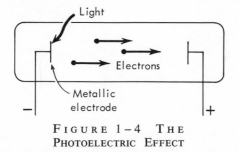

FIGURE 1–4   THE
PHOTOELECTRIC EFFECT

In 1887 Hertz discovered that light incident upon a metallic electrode caused emission of electrons[2] from that metal (photoelectric effect, see Figure 1–4). There are several particularly puzzling features that arise in connection with the photoelectric effect. One is that these electrons are emitted as soon as the light strikes the metallic electrode. Secondly, while the number of electrons emitted changes with the strength of the light (light intensity), the average energy of the electrons is independent of light

---

[2] It was not until 1897 that J. J. Thomson discovered the electron, and it was in 1899 that these particles were identified.

intensity. More intense radiation causes more electrons to be emitted than weak radiation, but it does not change the energy of the electrons. Moreover, changes in the frequency of the incident light do cause changes in the electronic energy. It was found that electrons were not emitted from the metal until the frequency of the radiation passed a certain threshold value ν_0. After this value, the energy of the electrons was found to be directly proportional to the frequency of the light.

In 1887 none of these facts could be explained. At that time light was considered to be a wavelike phenomenon. A wave striking the metal would hit many electrons, and a long time ought to be required before any one electron acquired sufficient energy to leave the metal. Also increasing the light intensity would supply more light and more energy to the irradiated region, and the departing electrons should have more energy.

In 1905, the same year he announced his theory of relativity, Einstein published his explanation of the photoelectric effect.[3] Sixteen years later in 1921, this declaration was to win for him the Nobel Prize for physics. Using the ideas announced by Planck in 1901, Einstein assumed that light of frequency ν had total energy content $E = nh\nu$. Thus, radiation of total energy equal to $nh\nu$ was considered to be made up of n discrete particles, each particle having an energy of $h\nu$. Lewis in 1926 called these particles photons. Light, then, consisted of photons, and these photons impinged upon an electronic target.

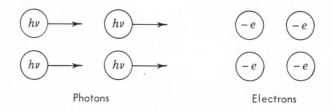

Photons   Electrons

Such an assumption explains quantitatively all the facts associated with the photoelectric effect. A photon hits an electron and is absorbed. If the energy $h\nu$ gained by the electron is sufficient, greater than $h\nu_0$, it can escape from the metal. This explains the observance of a threshold value below which no electrons are emitted. It also explains why no time delay is found. A photon hits, is absorbed by the electron, and the electron leaves. A more intense beam of light contains more photons, yet the energy content of each photon is still the same regardless of the light intensity. Therefore, intense radiation causes more electrons to depart but does not change the amount of energy an electron can acquire.

---

[3] A. Einstein, *Ann. Physik*, **17**, 132 (1905).

An electron acquires energy $h\nu$. If it is an electron in the interior of the metal, it may lose some of this energy in getting to the surface. An electron that is already on the surface of the metal does not have this problem. Thus the maximum energy an emitted electron can have, E_{max}, is equal to the energy acquired, $h\nu$, minus the energy expended to free itself from the metallic surface holding it.

$$E_{max} = h\nu - w \qquad (1.16)$$

where w, the photoelectric work function, is the energy lost by a surface electron in freeing itself from its environment. This term is usually expressed in electron volts (ev).

If one measures how E_{max} varies with the frequency of the light and plots the results, the slope of the line should equal h, Planck's constant. This was done by Millikan in 1916, and a value of h was found, which agreed quantitatively with that obtained by Planck in his work on black-body radiation. Thus, Einstein, working on a completely different problem, was able to explain the photoelectric effect, and thereby confirm and extend Planck's theory of energy quantization.

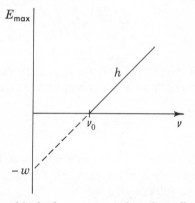

(the broken portion is hypothetical)

With this explanation of the photoelectric effect, Einstein presented the first example of what is known today as wave-particle dualism, that is, that a substance may manifest itself as a wave under some circumstances and as a particle under others.

4. WAVE-PARTICLE DUALISM

In 1924, at the age of 32, de Broglie submitted his doctoral dissertation "Investigations into Quantum Theory." Therein he set forth the concept of wave-particle dualism,[4] that a substance may display wavelike properties under some conditions and particlelike properties under others. We have encountered wave-particle dualism previously in connection with the photoelectric effect.

In order to explain diffraction experiments, light had to possess wavelike properties, yet it had been clearly demonstrated that a particlelike picture of light was necessary in order to explain the photoelectric effect. De Broglie reasoned that if light which was generally regarded as a wave could also exhibit particlelike behavior, why could not those materials usually regarded as particles display wavelike properties. This consideration caused de Broglie to postulate that we can associate with any particle a wave, and that this wave, which he called a pilot wave, governs the motion of the particle much as the pilot of a ship or plane governs the motion of his craft (see Figure 1–5). Since a wave is spread out in space, there is some uncertainty in the position of the particle. However, the greater the amplitude of the wave, the greater the probability of finding the particle. The amplitude of the pilot wave is a measure of the position of the particle.

FIGURE 1–5   PILOT WAVE AND PARTICLE

Furthermore, de Broglie stated that for a particle having momentum p, the wavelength λ of its pilot wave was given by the expression

$$\lambda = \frac{h}{p} \tag{1.17}$$

where h is Planck's constant and p is the momentum, mv, of the particle. This expression is readily derived for photons. We shall need the following equation describing the velocity of a wave:

$$v = \nu\lambda \tag{1.18}$$

where v is the velocity of the wave, ν its frequency, and λ its wavelength. The number of centimeters traveled by a wave per second is equal to the number of wavelengths per second times their length. For a light wave $v = c$ and equation (1.18) becomes

$$c = \nu\lambda \tag{1.19}$$

---

[4] For a nonmathematical presentation of wave-particle dualism see L. de Broglie, *New Perspectives in Physics*, Basic Books, New York, 1962.

Let us now define k, the wave number, as $1/\lambda$. We shall use this quantity later in connection with the Bohr theory of the atom.

Since

$$k = \frac{1}{\lambda}$$

then equation (1.19) becomes

$$\nu = ck \qquad (1.20)$$

From Einstein's equation of relativity we have that for a photon

$$E = cp$$

and from his equation for the photoelectric effect,

$$E = h\nu$$

Equating these two

$$cp = h\nu$$

or

$$\frac{c}{\nu} = \frac{h}{p}$$

since

$$c = \nu\lambda$$

we get de Broglie's postulate

$$\lambda = \frac{h}{p}$$

Remember that for the case derived above $p = mc$ (see equation 1.13). The boldness of de Broglie's postulate lies in the assertion that equation (1.17) is a general one that holds for substances moving at any velocity. Henceforth, we shall associate with any particle a wave with wavelength given by equation (1.17).

5. CONFIRMATION OF DE BROGLIE'S POSTULATE

For a particle having only kinetic energy, $U = 0$ and

$$E = \frac{p^2}{2m}$$

or

$$p^2 = 2mE$$

then

$$p = \sqrt{2mE}$$

The de Broglie wavelength for such a particle is

$$\lambda = \frac{h}{p}$$

$$\lambda = \frac{h}{\sqrt{2mE}}$$

If our particle happens to be an electron that is no longer attached to an atom, we know its mass, and we can impart to the electron a measurable kinetic energy. Now is there a wave associated with the electron, and if so, does the wavelength of this wave equal the de Broglie wavelength? This question was asked and answered by two groups working independently. Davisson and Germer at Bell Laboratories and G. P. Thomson and Reid at the University of Aberdeen investigated this problem. We have

$$h = 6.63 \times 10^{-27} \text{ erg-sec}$$

and

$$m = 9.11 \times 10^{-28} \text{ grams}$$

For an electron having energy

$$E = 54.0 \text{ ev}$$

$$1 \text{ ev} = 1.60 \times 10^{-12} \text{ erg}$$

then

$$\lambda = \frac{6.63 \times 10^{-27}}{\sqrt{2 \times 9.11 \times 10^{-28} \times 54.0 \times 1.60 \times 10^{-12}}} \text{ cm}$$

$$\lambda = 1.67 \times 10^{-8} \text{ cm}$$

or

$$\lambda = 1.67 \text{ A (Ångstrom)}$$

Our predicted wavelength for an electron having an energy of 54 ev is 1.67 A. Since x-rays have wavelengths in this region, a technique similar to x-ray diffraction, which is employed to determine the wavelengths of x-rays, can be used for our electron. This was done and it was found that an electron did indeed exhibit wavelike properties. The observed value of λ for an electron with an energy of 54 ev was 1.65 A, in excellent agreement with the calculated value.

De Broglie's assumption has been verified, and in fact, the technique of electron diffraction has found common usage. Proton and neutron diffraction studies have since been carried out. These materials also act as waves under suitable circumstances.

Although classical theory had served to answer successfully a large number of problems, it could not account for phenomena such as relativity, black-body radiation, the photoelectric effect, or wave-particle duality. These problems were solved only at the expense of introducing new concepts that were completely at variance with the classical theory. It is important to realize that only with reluctance were these new ideas accepted. Classical physics had worked well. It was finally the overwhelming evidence that these new concepts were not *ad hoc* ideas that led to their acceptance, and it was by using the concepts of energy quantization and wave-particle duality that the structure of the atom was elucidated, for these same ideas led to the development of wave mechanics.

6. THE THEORY OF THE ATOM

The photoelectric effect illustrates that metals lose electrons upon irradiation. It then follows that the atoms of which the metal is composed contain electrons. Furthermore, atoms are neutral. Since they contain electrons, they must also contain a positive charge that is of equal magnitude to the negative charge. A neutral atom having negative charge $Q = -Ze$ must also have positive charge $Q = Ze$ where Z refers to the number of electrons that are present. This quantity is known as the atomic number. In addition, the mass of an atom is many times greater than the electronic mass. Even an atom of hydrogen, which contains only one electron, is 1837 times heavier than the electron. This makes it apparent that the mass of an atom must be associated with the positive charge, and the question then arises concerning the nature of this positive charge and the exact distribution of electrons within the atom.

6.1. THOMSON'S MODEL OF THE ATOM   A description of an atom was proposed by J. J. Thomson in 1898. He suggested that the atom was a sphere of uniform positive charge with a radius of 10^{-8} cm, within which the electrons were embedded (see Figure 1–6).

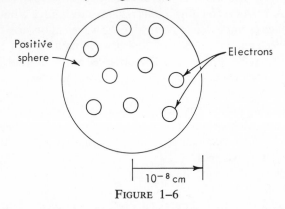

FIGURE 1–6

To check this theory Geiger and Marsden, working in Rutherford's laboratory, performed the following experiment as shown in Figure 1–7. A narrow beam of alpha particles, doubly ionized helium atoms, of known energy was directed upon a thin gold foil. A zinc sulfide screen was employed as a scintillation counter to indicate the position of the striking alpha particles. Most of the alpha particles passed through the gold foil undeflected and some were deflected at small angles, yet a significant number, about 1 percent, were scattered at large angles. It is this large angle scattering that is totally inconsistent with Thomson's model.

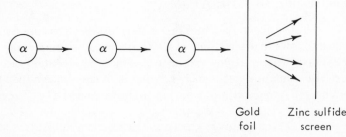

Gold foil

Zinc sulfide screen

FIGURE 1–7

In order for a rapidly moving alpha particle to be scattered through a large angle, a considerable repulsive force must be exerted. Thomson's model of the atom with its diffuse positive charge does not predict the existence of such a force. A region of concentrated positive charge and great mass is required. The Thomson model of the atom is necessarily incorrect.

6.2. RUTHERFORD'S MODEL OF THE ATOM

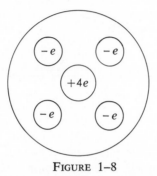

FIGURE 1–8

To explain the results of the Geiger-Marsden experiment, Rutherford was required to change the then-accepted picture of the atom. An atom, he concluded was mostly empty space, a tiny nucleus (approximately 10^{-13} cm) at the center containing most of the mass and all of the positive charge, and the several electrons located at various distances traveling around the nucleus (see Figure 1–8).

Now most of the alpha particles would travel through the empty space unaffected, also the electrons would have negligible effect upon the motion of the alpha particle. The momentum of an alpha particle, with mass approximately 7500 times greater than the mass of an electron, would remain essentially unchanged even in the presence of a nearby electron. As a result the force exerted on the alpha particle by an electron would not cause significant scattering.

$$F = \frac{dp_\alpha}{dt}$$

where p_α is the momentum of the alpha particle.

The picture is not the same when the alpha particle approaches a nucleus. Gold was the element used in the Geiger-Marsden experiment, and the gold nucleus with atomic number Z equal to 79 and mass approximately 50 times the mass of the alpha particle exerts considerable influence. This repulsive force causes a deflection of the alpha particle and accounts for the observed scattering. On the basis of his model, Rutherford calculated the distribution of alpha particles for various scattering angles θ (see Figure 1–9). The calculation for large scattering angles neglects electronic effects and considers deflection as being caused solely by Coulombic repulsion. Calculated results are in excellent agreement with experimental values.

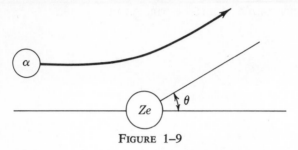

FIGURE 1–9

While Rutherford's hypothesis of a nuclear atom explained experimental results, it left physicists of the time a bit dismayed. According to classical electromagnetic theory, an electron undergoing acceleration, for example, traveling in an orbit about a positively charged nucleus, ought to lose energy and spiral into that nucleus.

6.3. BOHR'S MODEL OF THE ATOM

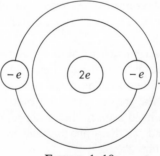

FIGURE 1–10

Bohr solved the problem for the physicist quite simply. Accepting Rutherford's idea of a nuclear atom forced him to conclude that an electron traveling in an orbit about a nucleus cannot spiral into that nucleus since atoms do exist. In any event, classical theory does not work on a microscopic scale. This had been demonstrated previously (black-body radiation, photoelectric effect). So Bohr postulated that an electron in its orbit does not lose energy, and since it loses no energy, it does not spiral into the nucleus. Secondly, he stated that an electron did gain or lose energy only in going from one orbit to another, and that this energy change, ΔE, was equal to $h\nu$. Finally, he assumed circular electronic orbits with quantized electronic angular momentum (see Figure 1-10).

$$L = \frac{nh}{2\pi} \qquad n = 1, 2, \cdot 3 \cdots \qquad (1.21)$$

Electrons traveled in circles with angular momentum equal to $nh/2\pi$ where n could not be zero and had to be an integer. Bohr had quantized the orbital angular momentum of the electron. Sommerfeld later extended this idea to include elliptical orbits. Equation (1.21) may be derived from de Broglie's postulate.

Allowed wavelength
Circumference = λ
$n = 1$

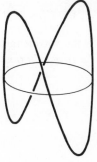

Allowed wavelength
Circumference = 2λ
$n = 2$

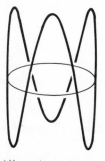

Allowed wavelength
Circumference = 3λ
$n = 3$

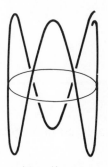

Not allowed

FIGURE 1-11 THE WAVELENGTHS OF THE
PILOT WAVES ASSOCIATED WITH A BOHR ORBIT

An electron in a Bohr orbit travels the circumference of the orbit, comes back to its starting position, and begins the same orbit again. If we are to ascribe a wave to the electron, the Bohr orbit must allow an integral number of wavelengths; otherwise, when the electron comes back to its starting position, it will be unable to continue along the same path. The wave will be out of phase and so destroy itself (see Figure 1–11). The circumference of each allowable Bohr orbit must contain an integral number of de Broglie wavelengths.

$$\text{Circumference} = 2\pi r$$

where r is the allowed radius and the distance of the electron from the nucleus. Therefore,

$$2\pi r = n\lambda \qquad n = 1, 2, 3 \cdots \qquad (1.22)$$

where λ is the wavelength of the wave associated with the electron.
From de Broglie's postulate

$$\lambda = \frac{h}{p}$$

or

$$\lambda = \frac{h}{mv}$$

Substituting this expression for λ into equation (1.22),

$$2\pi r = \frac{nh}{mv}$$

then

$$mvr = \frac{nh}{2\pi}$$

Now, mvr is just the angular momentum L (see equation 1.2) and we obtain

$$L = \frac{nh}{2\pi} \qquad n = 1, 2, 3 \cdots$$

Application of de Broglie's postulate to the electron in a Bohr orbit gives rise to the quantization of orbital angular momentum, yet this same equation was used by Bohr without theoretical justification. It is interesting to note that de Broglie published his work in 1924, while Bohr stated his ideas in 1913, fully 11 years prior to de Broglie.

Bohr solved the conflict with classical theory by stating that classical theory did not apply on the atomic level. His ideas had no prior theoretical justification, but the acceptance of any theory depends on whether or not it explains experimental results.

Before seeing just how Bohr was able to get his ideas accepted, let us consider the case of the hydrogen atom and see just what Bohr's postulates imply (see Figure 1–12).

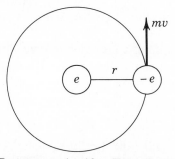

FIGURE 1 – 12   THE   BOHR
MODEL OF THE HYDROGEN ATOM

The hydrogen atom, according to Bohr, consists of a proton and an electron with the latter describing a circular path. As it travels along its orbit, the electron experiences an attractive force towards the center. This force — the electrostatic attraction between opposite charges — is just the Coulombic force e^2/r^2. (For this discussion we assume that all forces are positive.) Now, according to Newton's second law,

$$F = ma$$

or

$$\frac{e^2}{r^2} = ma \tag{1.23}$$

We know the mass of the electron but must find the acceleration. The acceleration experienced by this electron is the centripetal acceleration which may be obtained in the following way (see Figure 1–13). Let us construct a coordinate system with its origin at the nucleus of our atom. Now, as the electron travels once around its orbit, it traverses a distance $2\pi r$ where r is

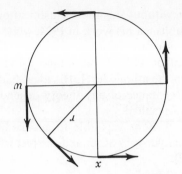

FIGURE 1–13   THE CHANGE IN THE VELOCITY VECTOR
AS THE ELECTRON TRAVELS ALONG A BOHR ORBIT

the radius of the orbit, and it does this in time T. The magnitude of the velocity v of the electron is the distance divided by the time.

$$v = \frac{2\pi r}{T} \tag{1.24}$$

The velocity is a vector quantity **v**, whose magnitude v does not change as the electron travels along the circle; only the direction of the velocity, which is always tangential to the circle, changes. Furthermore, the velocity vector is the product of the magnitude and a direction vector. In going from the point w to the point x, the change in the velocity Δv equals the magnitude of the velocity times the change in the direction $\pi/2$.

$$\Delta v = v\frac{\pi}{2}$$

In going around the circle once, the total change is

$$\Delta v = v2\pi$$

Again the time required for a complete revolution by the electron is T. Therefore

$$\frac{\Delta v}{\Delta t} = v\frac{2\pi}{T}$$

Since

$$a = \frac{\Delta v}{\Delta t}$$

we obtain

$$a = v\frac{2\pi}{T}$$

but from equation (1.24)

$$\frac{v}{r} = \frac{2\pi}{T}$$

then

$$a = (v)\left(\frac{v}{r}\right)$$

or

$$a = \frac{v^2}{r}$$

This is the centripetal acceleration where v is the magnitude of the electronic velocity and r the orbital radius. Substitution of this expression into equation (1.23) yields

$$\frac{e^2}{r^2} = \frac{mv^2}{r}$$

or

$$mv^2r = e^2 \qquad (1.25)$$

In addition, the angular momentum is given by equation (1.2) as

$$L = mvr$$

This was quantized by Bohr

$$L = \frac{nh}{2\pi} \qquad n = 1, 2, 3\cdots$$

Therefore

$$mvr = \frac{nh}{2\pi}$$

Solving this for v,

$$v = \frac{nh}{2\pi mr}$$

and squaring both sides of this equation,

$$v^2 = \frac{n^2h^2}{4\pi^2m^2r^2}$$

Substituting this expression for v^2 into equation (1.25), we obtain

$$\frac{n^2h^2}{4\pi^2mr} = e^2$$

or

$$r = \frac{h^2n^2}{4\pi^2me^2}$$

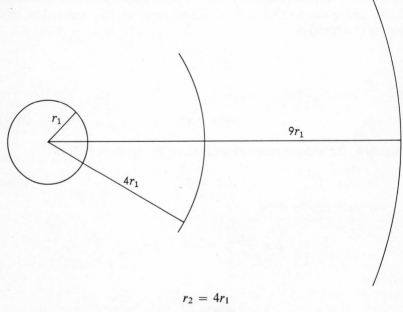

$$r_2 = 4r_1$$

$$r_3 = 9r_1$$

$$r_{\ddot{n}} = n^2r_1$$

FIGURE 1–14

Quantizing the angular momentum quantizes the allowable Bohr orbits.

$$= \frac{h^2}{4\pi^2 me^2} \times n^2 \qquad n = 1, 2, 3 \cdots \qquad (1.26)$$

The term $h^2/(4\pi^2 me^2)$ may be evaluated since Planck's constant h, the electronic mass m, and the value of e are all known.

$$\frac{h^2}{4\pi^2 me^2} = 0.53 \times 10^{-8} \text{ cm}$$

$$r = 0.53 \times 10^{-8} \times n^2 \qquad (1.27)$$

The energy of the electron is a minimum when it is in the smallest Bohr orbit (see Figure 1–14). This corresponds to $n = 1$ and $r_1 = 0.53 \times 10^{-8}$ cm. For the first excited state $n = 2$ and $r_2 = 4r_1 = 2.12 \times 10^{-8}$ cm.

Having found the orbits, let us find the energy of the hydrogen atom when the electron is in each orbit. The total energy of the hydrogen atom is

$$E = T + U$$

$$E = \frac{mv^2}{2} - \frac{e^2}{r}$$

Returning to equation (1.25), we have

$$mv^2 r = e^2$$

or

$$mv^2 = \frac{e^2}{r} \qquad (1.28)$$

Since the kinetic energy of the electron is given by

$$T = \frac{mv^2}{2}$$

we have from equation (1.28)

$$T = \frac{e^2}{2r}$$

Since

$$E = T + U$$

we find that

$$E = \frac{e^2}{2r} - \frac{e^2}{r}$$

or

$$E = -\frac{e^2}{2r} \tag{1.29}$$

Substituting from equation (1.26) for r

$$E = -\frac{2\pi^2 m e^4}{h^2 n^2}$$

then

$$E = -\frac{2\pi^2 m e^4}{h^2} \left(\frac{1}{n^2}\right) \qquad n = 1, 2, 3\cdots$$

We have quantized the total energy of the hydrogen atom. The ground state energy is

$$E_1 = -\frac{2\pi^2 m e^4}{h^2} \tag{1.30}$$

while

$$E_2 = -\frac{2\pi^2 m e^4}{h^2} \left(\frac{1}{4}\right) = \frac{1}{4} E_1$$

and

$$E_n = \frac{E_1}{n^2}$$

Notice that E is negative. This must be so since the hydrogen atom represents a stable system. The energy of an excited state, E_n, is also negative, but less negative than the ground state. Excited states are less stable. The ground-state energy of the hydrogen atom may be calculated from equation (1.30) or evaluated experimentally. The value is the negative of the ionization potential (the energy required to remove the electron).

$$E_1 = -13.6 \text{ ev}$$

$$E_2 = \frac{E_1}{4} = -3.4 \text{ ev}$$

$$E_3 = \frac{E_1}{9} = -1.5 \text{ ev}$$

$$E_n = -\frac{13.6 \text{ ev}}{n^2}$$

We have

$$E_n = \frac{E_1}{n^2}$$

and $$n = 1, 2, 3 \cdots$$

$$r_n = n^2 r_1$$

An electron in the ground state is in orbit r_1 and the system has energy E_1. For the first excited state, $n = 2$, the electron is in orbit r_2 with energy E_2, and so forth.

Quantization of the orbital angular momentum has led to quantization of orbits and consequently to quantization of the total energy of the hydrogen atom.

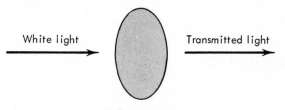

White light   Transmitted light

Hydrogen atoms

FIGURE 1–15   ABSORPTION OF
LIGHT BY HYDROGEN ATOMS

Having discussed Bohr's postulates, let us see how Bohr was able to get these ideas accepted. A problem that had long plagued physicists, and one which Bohr was able to answer, was that of the atomic spectrum of hydrogen.[5]

Consider the atoms of some element in the gaseous state, hydrogen, for example. It was known that irradiation of hydrogen atoms using white

---

[5] For a full discussion of atomic spectra, see G. Herzberg, *Atomic Spectra and Atomic structure*, Dover, New York, 1944.

light led to the absorption of certain discrete wavelengths, absorption spectrum (see Figure 1–15). In addition, hydrogen atoms excited by the passage of an electric current emitted light of certain wavelengths, emission spectrum.

Bohr explained these facts in the following way: an atom absorbs light and uses the energy to put the electron into an outer orbit. Alternatively, an excited hydrogen atom has the electron in an outer orbit. This excess energy is given off in the form of light emission, the electron moves to an inner orbit, and the system becomes more stable. Considering the emission spectrum of hydrogen, we start with the excited hydrogen atom in an initial state n_i with energy E_{n_i}. Energy in the form of light radiation (a photon) is emitted and the atom goes to final state n_f with energy E_{n_f} where n_f is less than n_i. The accompanying energy change, ΔE, for this process is

$$\Delta E = E_{n_i} - E_{n_f} \qquad n_f < n_i$$

or

$$\Delta E = \frac{E_1}{n_i{}^2} - \frac{E_1}{n_f{}^2}$$

then

$$\Delta E = E_1 \left(\frac{1}{n_i{}^2} - \frac{1}{n_f{}^2} \right)$$

and from equation (1.30)

$$\Delta E = -\frac{2\pi^2 m e^4}{h^2} \left(\frac{1}{n_i{}^2} - \frac{1}{n_f{}^2} \right)$$

Placing the minus sign inside the parentheses:

$$\Delta E = \frac{2\pi^2 m e^4}{h^2} \left(-\frac{1}{n_i{}^2} + \frac{1}{n_f{}^2} \right)$$

The final result is

$$\Delta E = \frac{2\pi^2 m e^4}{h^2} \left(\frac{1}{n_f{}^2} - \frac{1}{n_i{}^2} \right) \qquad n_f < n_i \qquad n = 1, 2, 3 \cdots$$

The hydrogen atom emits light and becomes more stable. The energy of the emitted light must equal the loss in energy by the hydrogen atom. Therefore, the energy of the photon equals ΔE. The frequency of a photon having energy ΔE may be obtained from Einstein's equation for the photoelectric effect.

$$\Delta E = h\nu$$

or

$$\Delta E = h\nu = \frac{2\pi^2 m e^4}{h^2}\left(\frac{1}{n_f^2} - \frac{1}{n_i^2}\right)$$

Solving for ν

$$\nu = \frac{2\pi^2 m e^4}{h^3}\left(\frac{1}{n_f^2} - \frac{1}{n_i^2}\right)$$

Using equation (1.20), in terms of the wave number k

$$k = \frac{2\pi^2 m e^4}{ch^3}\left(\frac{1}{n_f^2} - \frac{1}{n_i^2}\right)$$

Evaluation of the quantity $(2\pi^2 m e^4)/(ch^3)$ yields 109,737 cm^{-1}.

Analysis of spectroscopic data had led Balmer in 1885 to postulate an empirical equation of the type

$$k = R\left(\frac{1}{2^2} - \frac{1}{n_i^2}\right) \qquad \begin{array}{l} n_f = 2 \\ n_i > 2 \end{array}$$

where R is the Rydberg constant. This equation had no theoretical justification, but it explained the emission spectrum of hydrogen in the visible region. Experimental evaluation of R leads to the value

$$R = 109,677 \text{ cm}^{-1}$$

nearly the same value obtained by Bohr on a theoretical basis.

This striking success of the Bohr theory in explaining the atomic spectrum of hydrogen was the chief reason for its rapid acceptance.

6.4. THE CORRESPONDENCE PRINCIPLE   Classical physics works for large systems; it is only on the atomic level that it fails. The correspondence principle requires that quantum physics give the same results that classical physics does in the limit of large quantum numbers, that is, when applied to large systems.

We have discussed some of the principles used in classical physics. These principles were inadequate. They could not explain certain experimental observations, particularly on the microscopic level. To explain observed phenomena new ideas were required, ideas such as relativity, quantization, and wave-particle duality. Some of the postulates just discussed have withstood the test of time; others have been replaced. The old quantum theory of Bohr is gone. This theory assumed a planar hydrogen atom, yet the hydrogen atom might be expected to be three-dimensional; while it worked well for one element it was unable to explain accurately the atomic spectrum of any other element. In place of the Bohr theory, we have the modern theories of matrix and wave mechanics, formulated independently by Heisenberg and Schrödinger in 1925 and 1926. Wave mechanics, as we shall see, also uses the ideas of wave-particle duality and energy quantization.

PROBLEMS

1. Set up the Hamiltonian for $_3$Li.

2. Set up the Hamiltonian for the He_2^+ molecule.

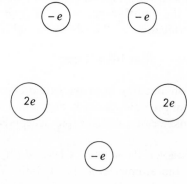

3. Give the expression for the potential energy of one of the electrons in $_4$Be.

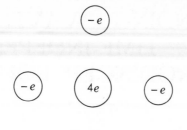

4. (a) Calculate the expected de Broglie wavelength of a proton having an energy of 54 ev (assume the mass of a proton to be 2000 times the mass of an electron).

(b) Predict the de Broglie wavelength of an electron with an energy of 500 ev.

(c) Why do you think low energy electrons were used in the early diffraction experiments?

5. The photoelectric work function of potassium is 2.0 ev. Assuming that $U = 0$,

(a) What is the maximum possible energy, in ev, of an electron emitted from a potassium surface when light of wavelength 4000 A (4×10^{-5} cm) irradiates the surface? (The velocity of light is 3×10^{10} cm/sec.)

(b) What is the linear momentum of an electron having this energy?

Chapter Two

STANDING WAVES AND THE TIME-INDEPENDENT SCHRÖDINGER EQUATION

1. WAVE DESCRIPTION

It was de Broglie's postulate on wave-particle duality that led Schrödinger to develop his theory of wave mechanics. At about the same time, in fact slightly earlier, Heisenberg, Born, and Jordan presented another formulation of quantum mechanics. This theory, known as matrix mechanics, does not depend upon de Broglie's postulate. Instead, the usual quantities such as position, momentum, and energy are represented by matrices, and equations of motion become matrix equations.

Although the two representations are conceptually quite different, their mathematical equivalence was demonstrated in 1926 by Schrödinger.[1]

We begin by discussing a simple sine wave and formulating the equation that describes this wave (see Figure 2–1). A sine wave where the value of psi (ψ) is a function of the position x alone is describable as

$$\psi = A \sin bx$$

Here A is the maximum value of ψ, and b is a constant that depends upon the wave in question. This constant can be expressed in terms of the wavelength λ of the wave.

To evaluate b, we start with the wave at the origin. At this point the function, $\psi = A \sin bx$, is equal to zero. Furthermore, this function attains

---

[1] E. Schrödinger, *Ann. Physik*, **79**, 734 (1926).

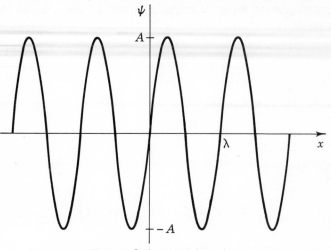

FIGURE 2–1 $\psi = A$ SIN bx

its maximum value at $bx = \pi/2$; it has another zero at $bx = \pi$, a minimum at $bx = 3\pi/2$, and a zero again at $bx = 2\pi$. Now the distance, as measured along the x axis, from the origin to the point $bx = 2\pi$ is equal to one wavelength λ. At the point where $bx = 2\pi$, x is equal to λ.

$$bx = 2\pi$$

yet here

$$x = \lambda$$

therefore

$$b = \frac{2\pi}{\lambda}$$

Substituting for b into the original equation gives the result,

$$\psi = A \sin \frac{2\pi x}{\lambda}$$

which gives an expression for the sine wave in terms of its wavelength.

We have described a sine wave. A cosine wave can be described in an analogous fashion,

$$\psi = B \cos \frac{2\pi x}{\lambda}$$

and a more general wave description is simply the sum of these two expressions.

$$\psi = A \sin \frac{2\pi x}{\lambda} + B \cos \frac{2\pi x}{\lambda} \tag{2.1}$$

In terms of the wave number

$$k = \frac{1}{\lambda}$$

we have

$$\psi = A \sin 2\pi kx + B \cos 2\pi kx \tag{2.2}$$

2. TIME-INDEPENDENT SCHRÖDINGER EQUATION

We are now in a position to obtain the time-independent Schrödinger equation. This expression cannot be derived from classical mechanics for it is outside the realm of that subject. We develop here the Schrödinger equation for a simple particle. The particle in question will usually be an electron, and we shall be interested in finding the energy of the electron. Having found it, unless some change occurs, we can naturally assume that this energy remains constant. The electron will have constant total energy. Its kinetic energy may vary as it travels, as may its potential energy, but its total energy remains constant.

$$E = T + U$$

where E is constant. The simplest approach is to develop the Schrödinger equation in one dimension for a single particle having constant kinetic and potential energy, then to generalize the result to three dimensions, and finally to allow variable kinetic and potential energy.

Imagine an electron of constant kinetic and constant potential energy, and assume that the motion of this electron is restricted to a region of the x axis. We are interested in the total energy of the electron, and if possible the positions at which it is likely to be found. Associated with the electron is its wave, and to describe our particle we need only describe this associated wave. But we have an equation that describes a wave on the x axis. Equation (2.1) describes just such a wave. Since it fulfills our requirements, the wave represented by this equation must be the wave associated with our electron. The value of ψ at any point is related to the probability of finding the electron at that point, and the values of A, B, and λ depend upon the particle in question. Acceptance of the idea of wave-particle duality requires that the energy of the electron be expressible as the energy of the associated wave, and that the momentum and position of the particle also be related to the wave. De Broglie's postulate, equation (1.17), relates the momentum of the particle to the wavelength of the wave

$$\lambda = \frac{h}{p}$$

and Einstein's equation gives the energy of the wave and therefore, of the particle in terms of the wave frequency.

$$E = h\nu$$

or

$$\nu = \frac{E}{h} \tag{2.3}$$

Returning to equation (2.1), we may replace the wavelength by de Broglie's equivalent h/p.

$$\psi = A \sin \frac{2\pi p x}{h} + B \cos \frac{2\pi p x}{h} \tag{2.4}$$

There are various equivalent forms which this equation may take. We have already seen that it may be expressed as in equations (2.1) and (2.2). Here is a third representation. Still another stems from the fact that the Hamiltonian for an electron of total energy E, kinetic energy T, and potential energy U, is given by the expression

$$H = E = T + U$$

$$H = E = \frac{p^2}{2m} + U \tag{2.5}$$

or

$$\frac{p^2}{2m} = E - U$$

then

$$p = \sqrt{2m(E - U)}$$

Substitution for p in equation (2.4) leads to

$$\psi = A \sin \frac{2\pi}{h} \sqrt{2m(E - U)}x + B \cos \frac{2\pi}{h} \sqrt{2m(E - U)}x \qquad (2.6)$$

The Schrödinger equation for our particle is a differential equation whose solution is a wave of the type (2.4). By large values of ψ we mean large in a negative as well as large in a positive sense, and the larger the value of ψ, the greater is the probability of finding the electron.

The Schrödinger equation must be consistent with equation (2.5) and have as its solution equation (2.4). The problem becomes one of finding the differential equation which satisfies these conditions.

Multiplication of both sides of equation (2.5) by ψ does not destroy the equality and yields

$$E\psi = \left(\frac{p^2}{2m} + U \right)\psi \qquad (2.7)$$

or

$$E\psi = \frac{p^2}{2m}\psi + U\psi$$

transposing

$$\frac{p^2}{2m}\psi = (E - U)\psi \qquad (2.8)$$

Now if we differentiate ψ in equation (2.4) twice with respect to x, we obtain the following:

$$\psi = A \sin \frac{2\pi px}{h} + B \cos \frac{2\pi px}{h}$$

$$\frac{\partial \psi}{\partial x} = \frac{2\pi p}{h} \left[A \cdot \cos \frac{2\pi px}{h} - B \sin \frac{2\pi px}{h} \right]$$

$$\frac{\partial^2 \psi}{\partial x^2} = \frac{4\pi^2 p^2}{h^2} \left[-A \sin \frac{2\pi px}{h} - B \cos \frac{2\pi px}{h} \right]$$

Placing the minus sign outside of the brackets

$$\frac{\partial^2 \psi}{\partial x^2} = -\frac{4\pi^2 p^2}{h^2} \left[A \sin \frac{2\pi px}{h} + B \cos \frac{2\pi px}{h} \right]$$

The expression inside the brackets is simply ψ and therefore

$$\frac{\partial^2 \psi}{\partial x^2} = -\frac{4\pi^2}{h^2} p^2 \psi$$

Solving for $p^2\psi$

$$p^2\psi = -\frac{h^2}{4\pi^2} \frac{\partial^2 \psi}{\partial x^2}$$

Dividing both sides by $2m$

$$\frac{p^2\psi}{2m} = -\frac{h^2}{8\pi^2 m} \frac{\partial^2 \psi}{\partial x^2} \tag{2.9}$$

Substituting equation (2.9) for $p^2\psi/2m$ into equation (2.8) we get

$$-\frac{h^2}{8\pi^2 m} \frac{\partial^2 \psi}{\partial x^2} = (E - U)\psi$$

or

$$-\frac{h^2}{8\pi^2 m} \frac{\partial^2 \psi}{\partial x^2} + U\psi = E\psi \tag{2.10}$$

This is the one dimensional Schrödinger equation for a single particle. We may factor ψ out of the left-hand side of equation (2.10)

$$\left[-\frac{h^2}{8\pi^2 m} \frac{\partial^2}{\partial x^2} + U \right]\psi = E\psi \tag{2.11}$$

This is merely a mathematical symbolism or shorthand. It is convenient, for it saves space and time. The equation remains unaltered, but ψ need be written only once. Comparison of equation (2.11) with equation (2.7) shows that we have replaced p^2 by an operator equivalent.

$$p^2 = -\frac{h^2}{4\pi^2} \frac{\partial^2}{\partial x^2} \tag{2.12}$$

Comparison of equation (2.11) with equation (2.5) indicates that H has also been replaced by an operator equivalent. This operator is called the Hamiltonian operator.

$$H = -\frac{h^2}{8\pi^2 m} \frac{\partial^2}{\partial x^2} + U \tag{2.13}$$

The procedure usually followed is to set up the classical Hamiltonian for a system, multiply the expression by ψ, and convert to quantum mechanics by replacing p^2 wherever it occurs by its operator equivalent.

Equation (2.11) may be written in operator form as

$$H\psi = E\psi \tag{2.14}$$

where H is the one-dimensional Hamiltonian operator. The energy E of the electron is called the eigenvalue, and ψ is called the eigenfunction. Remember that the eigenfunction merely represents the wave associated with our electron.

Extending the Schrödinger equation to three dimensions we obtain

$$\left[-\frac{h^2}{8\pi^2 m}\frac{\partial^2}{\partial x^2} - \frac{h^2}{8\pi^2 m}\frac{\partial^2}{\partial y^2} - \frac{h^2}{8\pi^2 m}\frac{\partial^2}{\partial z^2} + U \right]\psi = E\psi$$

or

$$-\frac{h^2}{8\pi^2 m}\left[\frac{\partial^2 \psi}{\partial x^2} + \frac{\partial^2 \psi}{\partial y^2} + \frac{\partial^2 \psi}{\partial z^2} \right] + U\psi = E\psi$$

The motion of the electron is no longer restricted to the x axis and the p^2 operator now contains terms for the y and z axes.

$$p^2 = -\frac{h^2}{4\pi^2}\left[\frac{\partial^2}{\partial x^2} + \frac{\partial^2}{\partial y^2} + \frac{\partial^2}{\partial z^2} \right]$$

The three-dimensional Hamiltonian operator is

$$H = -\frac{h^2}{8\pi^2 m}\left[\frac{\partial^2}{\partial x^2} + \frac{\partial^2}{\partial y^2} + \frac{\partial^2}{\partial z^2} \right] + U$$

In terms of this operator we may still write the Schrödinger equation as

$$H\psi = E\psi \tag{2.15}$$

where H is now the three-dimensional Hamiltonian operator and ψ is now a function of x, y, and z, $\psi = \psi(x, y, z)$. This equation was obtained by assuming constant kinetic and potential energy terms. We may safely assume that it holds in every case where the value of E remains constant.

Equation (2.15) holds special significance for the chemist. The eigenfunctions ψ are the orbitals that are familiar to all chemists. Equation (2.15) states that an electron in orbital ψ has energy E. Although we have given added significance to ψ, its original meaning does not change. It is still the wave that we associate with our electron, only we call this wave an eigenfunction or an orbital. An electron in a molecular orbital ψ will have energy E. If the electron is in an s atomic orbital, then our equation reads

$$Hs = Es$$

where E is now the energy of the electron in that particular s orbital. For a p orbital, we have

$$Hp = Ep \tag{2.16}$$

where E is the energy of an electron in that p atomic orbital.

3. PROBABILITY, ORTHONORMALITY, AND DEGENERACY

We are going to associate the value of ψ at a point (x, y, z) with the probability of finding the electron there.

Probability varies between the limits zero and one. Zero implies no probability of finding the electron, that is, certainty of its absence, while one implies certainty of finding the electron. A probability of 0.5 states a 50 percent chance of finding the electron, 0.3 a 30 percent chance, and so forth. Notice that the probability is always positive. Now the value of ψ at a point may be either positive or negative (see Figure 2–1). Therefore, ψ itself cannot be a direct measure of the probability. We need a quantity that is always positive. The choice of ψ^2 seems reasonable as the square of any real number fits this requirement. It may appear somewhat arbitrary to relate ψ^2 to the probability of finding the electron. Naturally, this choice is subject to verification. If experimental evidence confirms this assumption, we continue to use ψ^2 rather than some other quantity. If and when data indicate that the choice is a poor one, we abandon it and search for another. It turns out that the choice of ψ^2 is not only reasonable but correct.

There are two interpretations that may be given ψ^2. One interpretation assumes the electron free to travel the entire universe and the value of ψ^2 at any point as the probability of finding the electron at that point. Of course, for most points in the universe the value of ψ^2 is pretty small. Such an approach was proposed by Born in 1926. The other interpretation assumes one electron spread over the entire universe and ψ^2 as the fraction of electron (electron density) at a point.

In a strict sense we cannot discuss the probability of finding the electron at some point. Instead we must speak of the probability of finding the electron in some small region. For a one-dimensional problem where we restrict the motion of the electron to the x axis, the probability of finding the electron in the region between x and $x + dx$ (or the election density in this region) is given by $\psi^2\, dx$, and the total probability of finding the electron on the x axis is given by the integral of this quantity.

$$\int_{-\infty}^{\infty} \psi^2\, dx$$

The value of this integral gives the probability of finding the electron on the x axis, which stretches from $-\infty$ to ∞. This must equal unity because we are certain of finding the electron here. Our initial assumption restricted the electron to this axis; therefore,

$$\int_{-\infty}^{\infty} \psi\psi\, dx = 1$$

(for a one-dimensional problem)

Analogously, for a three-dimensional problem $\psi^2\, dx\, dy\, dz$ yields the probability of finding the electron in the volume element $dx\, dy\, dz$ and the triple integral in equation (2.17) affords the probability of finding the electron somewhere in the universe. This must be unity, and

$$\int_{-\infty}^{\infty}\int_{-\infty}^{\infty}\int_{-\infty}^{\infty} \psi^2\, dx\, dy\, dz = 1 \tag{2.17}$$

(for a three-dimensional problem)

Equation (2.17) is called the normalization requirement. Whenever possible, one works with normalized ψ's, that is, ψ's which obey equation (2.17). We shall see later in the chapter how one gets normalized eigenfunctions. Equation (2.17) may be rewritten as

$$\int \psi\psi\, dv = 1 \tag{2.18}$$

where dv is the volume element $dx\, dy\, dz$ and the limits of integration are implicit. The requirement that ψ^2 be a probability places certain restrictions on ψ. First of all, probability is single-valued, that is, the probability of finding the electron cannot have two different values at the same position. Therefore, ψ^2 and ψ must be single-valued. Secondly, ψ must obey equation (2.18); this requires ψ to be everywhere finite. The value of ψ may never be infinite for that makes the value of the integral infinite. Thirdly, equation (2.18) requires integration of ψ; therefore continuity is desirous. In fact, the

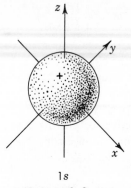

1s

FIGURE 2-2

probability of finding the electron must vary from point to point in a continuous fashion. Therefore, ψ^2 and ψ must be continuous.

The pictures that the chemist uses when describing electronic positions represent large values of ψ^2. The 1s orbital is pictured as a sphere with the nucleus at the center (see Figure 2–2). Every point within the sphere represents a large value of ψ^2. There is then a large but not certain probability of finding the electron within this sphere. There is also a small but finite probability of finding the electron outside the sphere.

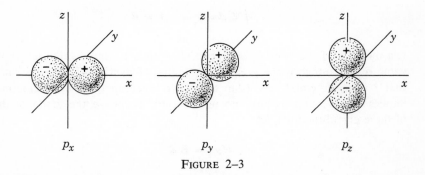

p_x p_y p_z

FIGURE 2-3

The plus and minus signs in Figure 2–3 indicate the sign of the eigenfunction in that region. The 1s eigenfunction is always positive while the p_x, p_y, and p_z eigenfunctions are positive for positive x, y, or z, but negative for negative x, y, z. The p_z orbital is the easiest to specify mathematically, and this is usually chosen when one works with p orbitals.

The mathematical descriptions of the normalized 1s and $2p_z$ orbitals in the hydrogen atom are

$$1s = \frac{1}{\sqrt{\pi}}\left(\frac{1}{a_o}\right)^{3/2} e^{-(r/a_o)}$$

$$2p_z = \frac{1}{4\sqrt{2\pi}}\left(\frac{1}{a_o}\right)^{5/2} e^{-(r/2a_o)}z \qquad (2.19)$$

where r is the distance of the electron from the nucleus and $a_o = h^2/(4\pi^2me^2)$ $= 0.53 \times 10^{-8}$ cm (see equation 1.27).

The value of the $1s$ orbital is dependent only on r and is always positive. (The distance is always positive.)

The $2p_z$ orbital is positive for positive z and negative for negative z, yet the probability of finding the electron at a point $+z$ is the same as the probability of finding the electron at $-z$, for $(2p_z)^2$ is the same regardless of the sign of $2p_z$.

Another interesting property of the eigenfunctions is their orthogonality. Consider two orbitals, ψ_A and ψ_B, for example, the $1s$ and $2s$ orbitals associated with a hydrogen atom. These functions are said to be orthogonal if the integral of their product is zero.

$$\int \psi_A\psi_B\, dv = 0 \qquad (2.20)$$

The value of the integral of the product, $\psi_A\psi_B$

$$\int \psi_A\psi_B\, dv \qquad A \neq B$$

is a measure of the overlap between the orbitals ψ_A and ψ_B, the larger the value of the integral, the greater the degree of overlap. The requirement that $\int \psi_A\psi_B\, dv$ equal zero (that these two eigenfunctions be orthogonal) implies that ψ_A and ψ_B have no net overlap. To prove the orthogonality of these eigenfunctions, let

$$H\psi_A = E_A\psi_A$$

and

$$H\psi_B = E_B\psi_B$$

where E_A is the energy of an electron in ψ_A, and E_B the energy of an electron in ψ_B. Now multiply the first equation by ψ_B and the second by ψ_A

$$\psi_B H\psi_A = \psi_B E_A\psi_A$$

$$\psi_A H\psi_B = \psi_A E_B\psi_B$$

Integration of all terms leads to

$$\int \psi_B H \psi_A \, dv = \int \psi_B E_A \psi_A \, dv = E_A \int \psi_B \psi_A \, dv \qquad (2.21)$$

$$\int \psi_A H \psi_B \, dv = \int \psi_A E_B \psi_B \, dv = E_B \int \psi_A \psi_B \, dv \qquad (2.22)$$

Since E_A and E_B are numbers, it is permissible to take them out from under the integral sign. The integrals on the left of equations (2.21) and (2.22) represent the energy of an electron associated with both ψ's. Even assuming the value of these integrals to be unknown, both must have the same value, whatever it is. The properties of H are such that both of these integrals must have the same value. Therefore,

$$\int \psi_A H \psi_B \, dv = \int \psi_B H \psi_A \, dv$$

also

$$\int \psi_A \psi_B \, dv = \int \psi_B \psi_A \, dv$$

Subtraction of equation (2.22) from (2.21) gives

$$0 = E_A \int \psi_A \psi_B \, dv - E_B \int \psi_A \psi_B \, dv$$

or

$$0 = (E_A - E_B) \int \psi_A \psi_B \, dv$$

Now, since E_A is in general not equal to E_B, the expression $(E_A - E_B)$ is not equal to zero. Therefore, in order for the above equation to hold, the value of the integral must equal zero.

$$\int \psi_A \psi_B \, dv = 0$$

This completes the proof concerning the orthogonality of the ψ's. The assumption that E_A is not equal to E_B is unnecessary. It may be shown that $\int \psi_A \psi_B \, dv = 0$, even in the case $E_A = E_B$.

If E_A does equal E_B, then ψ_A and ψ_B are said to be degenerate. Two eigenfunctions corresponding to the same eigenvalue are degenerate (two orbitals having the same energy).

$$H\psi_A = E_A\psi_A$$

$$H\psi_B = E_B\psi_B$$

but

$$E_B = E_A$$

consequently

$$H\psi_B = E_A\psi_B$$

A well-known example is the p atomic orbitals, which are threefold degenerate.

$$Hp_x = Ep_x$$

$$Hp_y = Ep_y$$

$$Hp_z = Ep_z$$

We have shown that there is no net overlap between two different atomic orbitals associated with the same atom or between two different molecular orbitals on the same molecule. The $1s$ orbital of a hydrogen atom is orthogonal to the $2s$ orbital of that same atom and both of these are orthogonal to the $2p_z$ orbital, and so forth. This result does not imply that there can be no overlap between orbitals associated with different atoms or molecules; for example, the $1s$ orbital on one hydrogen atom can and does overlap with the $1s$ orbital of another hydrogen atom to form the sigma bond in a hydrogen molecule, and the $1s$ atomic orbital of hydrogen can certainly overlap with a $3p$ atomic orbital associated with a chlorine atom to form a molecule of hydrogen chloride.

A set of functions that satisfies equations (2.18) and (2.20) is called an orthonormal set. Such a set may be expressed as follows:

$$\int \psi_A\psi_B \, dv = \begin{cases} 1 & A = B \\ 0 & A \neq B \end{cases}$$

4. PARTICLE IN A BOX

Before going on to molecular problems where one cannot obtain an exact solution to the Schrödinger equation, it is worthwhile to look at one or two cases where an exact solution is possible. The ideas of energy quantization, normalization, and orthogonality are adequately demonstrated in these simple situations.

Consider a particle constrained to travel in a one-dimensional box of length L. This may be done by assuming that the potential energy of the particle is zero when it is inside the box and infinite outside the box. Since it is impossible for the particle to enter into the region where it must have infinite potential energy, the particle can never leave the box. We are interested in the quantum mechanically allowed energy levels of the particle; these will be kinetic energy levels ($U = 0$), and the shape of the eigenfunctions corresponding to each energy level.

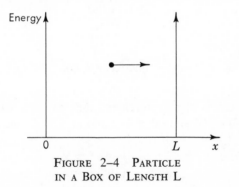

FIGURE 2–4 PARTICLE
IN A BOX OF LENGTH L

Since ψ^2 is the probability of finding the particle at any point, and since it is certain that the particle cannot leave the box, ψ^2 must be zero at the boundaries of the box and everywhere outside the box. Therefore, ψ is zero at the boundaries and outside the box (see Figure 2–4).

$$\psi = 0 \begin{cases} -\infty < x \leq 0 \\ L \leq x < \infty \end{cases} \tag{2.23}$$

This is a one-dimensional problem, and the one-dimensional Schrödinger equation is from equation (2.10)

$$H\psi = E\psi$$

or

$$-\frac{h^2}{8\pi^2 m}\frac{\partial^2\psi}{\partial x^2} + U\psi = E\psi$$

We already know the solution to this differential equation. It is an equation of the type (2.4).

$$\psi = A \sin\frac{2\pi px}{h} + B \cos\frac{2\pi px}{h}$$

For the particle inside the box $U = 0$, and

$$E = \frac{p^2}{2m}$$

or

$$p = \sqrt{2mE}$$

therefore

$$\psi = A \sin\frac{2\pi}{h}\sqrt{2mE}x + B \cos\frac{2\pi}{h}\sqrt{2mE}x \qquad (2.24)$$

In addition, there is the requirement that the eigenfunction given by expression (2.24) equal zero at $x = 0$ and at $x = L$ (see expression 2.23).

$$\psi = 0 \begin{cases} \text{at } x = 0 \\ \text{and } x = L \end{cases}$$

Substitution of $x = 0$, $\psi = 0$ into equation (2.24) gives

$$0 = A \sin 0 + B \cos 0$$

The sine of 0 is zero, but the cosine of 0 is one. Therefore, in order to satisfy our boundary conditions (equation 2.23), B must be zero and

$$\psi = A \sin\frac{2\pi}{h}\sqrt{2mE}x \qquad (2.25)$$

Similarly, evaluation of our equation at $x = L$ affords

$$0 = A \sin\frac{2\pi}{h}\sqrt{2mE}L \qquad (2.26)$$

This condition can be satisfied only if

$$\frac{2\pi}{h}\sqrt{2mEL} = n\pi \qquad n = 1, 2, 3, \cdots$$

for it is only the sine of π, 2π, 3π, and so forth, that is zero. It is here that quantization is introduced in order to satisfy equation (2.26). It is not possible for the quantum number n to equal zero. In that case, ψ is zero everywhere. This means that ψ^2 is zero everywhere, and there is no particle. But this contradicts our initial assumption that there is a particle. Therefore n cannot be zero. If

$$\frac{2\pi}{h}\sqrt{2mEL} = n\pi$$

dividing both sides by L

$$\frac{2\pi}{h}\sqrt{2mE} = \frac{n\pi}{L}$$

and substituting this expression into equation (2.25), we obtain:

$$\psi_n = A \sin\frac{n\pi x}{L} \qquad n = 1, 2, 3\cdots \qquad (2.27)$$

These are the eigenfunctions for the particle in a box. Furthermore, if

$$\frac{2\pi}{h}\sqrt{2mEL} = n\pi$$

then

$$E_n = \frac{n^2h^2}{8mL^2} \qquad n = 1, 2, 3\cdots \qquad (2.28)$$

The possible orbitals for our particle are given by equation (2.27) and the energy associated with each orbital by equation (2.28). We plot the orbitals in Figure 2–5.

In the ground state, the particle will have energy E_1 and occupy orbital ψ_1; for the first excited state it will have energy E_2 and occupy ψ_2, and so forth. Figure 2–5 illustrates that as the energy of the particle increases, so does the number of nodes in the eigenfunction. Increasing the number of nodes (decreasing λ) corresponds to increasing the kinetic energy (see equation 1.17).

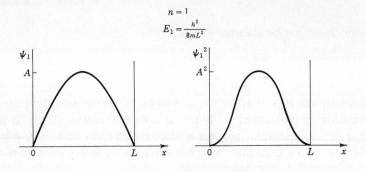

$$n = 1$$
$$E_1 = \frac{h^2}{8mL^2}$$

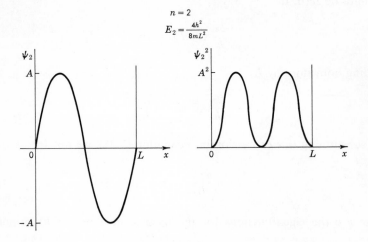

$$n = 2$$
$$E_2 = \frac{4h^2}{8mL^2}$$

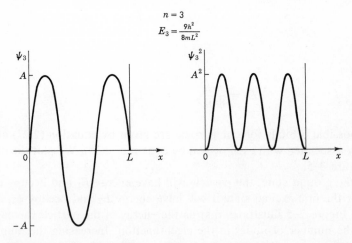

$$n = 3$$
$$E_3 = \frac{9h^2}{8mL^2}$$

FIGURE 2–5 THE FIRST THREE EIGENVALUES AND THE CORRESPONDING EIGENFUNCTIONS FOR THE PARTICLE IN A BOX

Notice that the probability of finding the particle at some point varies with the energy of the particle. A particle having energy E_1 is most likely to be found at the center of the box, whereas a particle with energy E_2 may never be found at that spot. According to quantum mechanics, a particle in a box of given length L must have energy. It cannot be inside the box and have zero energy. The minimum possible value is E_1 and this is called the zero point energy. The particle may be considered as vibrating between the walls of its enclosure, and the existence of zero point energy is a general phenomenon for vibrating systems.

Since the term L^2 appears in the denominator of equation (2.28), increasing L, the size of the box, stabilizes our particle. Assuming our particle to be an electron, this result implies that charge delocalization is a stabilizing factor, for example, tertiary carbonium ions are more stable than primary or secondary, and it is for this reason that the allyl and benzyl carbonium ions, radicals, and carbanions exhibit great stability.

The total eigenfunction for a particle having energy E_n is

$$\psi_n = \begin{cases} 0 & -\infty < x \leq 0 \\ A \sin \dfrac{n\pi x}{L} & 0 \leq x \leq L \\ 0 & L \leq x < \infty \end{cases} \qquad (2.29)$$

Having found the eigenfunctions for the particle in a box, we proceed to normalize them. Our normalization condition for a one-dimensional problem requires that

$$\int_{-\infty}^{\infty} \psi_n \psi_n dx = 1$$

This integral may be separated into three parts such that

$$\int_{-\infty}^{0} \psi_n{}^2 \, dx + \int_{0}^{L} \psi_n{}^2 \, dx + \int_{L}^{\infty} \psi_n{}^2 \, dx = 1$$

Now ψ_n is zero everywhere on the intervals covered by the first and third integrals (see equation 2.29). Therefore

$$\int_{-\infty}^{0} \psi_n{}^2 \, dx = \int_{L}^{\infty} \psi_n{}^2 \, dx = 0$$

and our normalization condition reduces to

$$\int_{0}^{L} \psi_n{}^2 \, dx = 1$$

Substituting for ψ_n,

$$\int_0^L \psi_n^2 \, dx = A^2 \int_0^L \sin^2 \frac{n\pi x}{L} \, dx = 1$$

then

$$A^2 \int_0^L \left(\frac{1 - \cos (2n\pi x)/L}{2} \right) dx = 1\dagger$$

Integrating this expression leads to

$$A^2 \frac{L}{2} = 1$$

or

$$A = \sqrt{\frac{2}{L}}$$

Normalization requires that $A = \sqrt{2/L}$, and our normalized eigenfunction for a particle having energy E_n becomes

$$\psi_n = \begin{cases} 0 & -\infty < x \leq 0 \\ \sqrt{\frac{2}{L}} \sin \frac{n\pi x}{L} & 0 \leq x \leq L \\ 0 & L \leq x < \infty \end{cases}$$

To illustrate the orthogonality of the eigenfunctions, we choose ψ_1 and ψ_2 and show that the

$$\int_{-\infty}^{\infty} \psi_1 \psi_2 \, dx = 0$$

This reduces to

$$\int_0^L \psi_1 \psi_2 \, dx = 0$$

---

† The integrand comes from the trigonometric identities

$$1 = \cos^2 \theta + \sin^2 \theta$$

and

$$\cos 2\theta = \cos^2 \theta - \sin^2 \theta$$

where

$$\psi_1 = \sqrt{\frac{2}{L}} \sin \frac{\pi x}{L}$$

$$\psi_2 = \sqrt{\frac{2}{L}} \sin \frac{2\pi x}{L}$$

We must show that

$$\frac{2}{L} \int_0^L \sin \frac{2\pi x}{L} \sin \frac{\pi x}{L} \, dx = 0$$

Now

$$\sin \frac{2\pi x}{L} = 2 \sin \frac{\pi x}{L} \cos \frac{\pi x}{L}$$

and our integral becomes

$$\frac{4}{L} \int_0^L \sin^2 \frac{\pi x}{L} \cos \frac{\pi x}{L} \, dx = 0$$

This is an integral of the type $u^2 \, du$ where

$$u = \sin \frac{\pi x}{L}$$

Integration yields

$$\frac{4}{3\pi} \sin^3 \frac{\pi x}{L} \Big|_0^L = 0$$

or

$$0 = 0$$

The eigenvalues for the particle in a box are given by equation (2.28). We present here an alternative method for obtaining these eigenvalues. The Schrödinger equation for a particle described by the eigenfunction ψ_n is

$$H\psi_n = E_n\psi_n$$

Multiplication of this expression by ψ_n yields,

$$\psi_n H \psi_n = \psi_n E_n \psi_n$$

and integration leads to the following equation,

$$\int \psi_n H \psi_n \, dx = \int \psi_n E_n \psi_n \, dx$$

Since E_n is simply a number representing the energy of the particle, we may take it out from under the integral sign. Then solving for E_n,

$$E_n = \frac{\int \psi_n H \psi_n \, dx}{\int \psi_n \psi_n \, dx}$$

We are interested in the allowed eigenvalues for a particle inside the box. Here x varies between 0 and L, and once again these are the limits of integration.

$$E_n = \frac{\int_0^L \psi_n H \psi_n \, dx}{\int_0^L \psi_n \psi_n \, dx}$$

Since ψ_n is normalized, the denominator is equal to unity. However, we need not take advantage of this fact. Furthermore, in this region ψ_n is given by

$$\psi_n = \sqrt{\frac{2}{L}} \sin \frac{n \pi x}{L}$$

Substitution of this quantity into the equation yields,

$$E_n = \frac{(2/L) \int_0^L \sin (n\pi x/L) \, H \sin (n\pi x/L) \, dx}{(2/L) \int_0^L \sin (n\pi x/L) \sin (n\pi x/L) \, dx}$$

Since for our particle $U = 0$, the Hamiltonian operator becomes

$$H = -\frac{h^2}{8\pi^2 m} \frac{\partial^2}{\partial x^2}$$

Let us replace the symbol H by its equivalent as given by this expression. Then

$$E_n = -\frac{h^2}{8\pi^2 m} \frac{\int_0^L \sin(n\pi x/L)\left(\frac{\partial^2 \sin(n\pi x/L)}{\partial x^2}\right) dx}{\int_0^L \sin(n\pi x/L)\sin(n\pi x/L)\, dx}$$

Carrying out the operation $\dfrac{\partial^2 \sin(n\pi x/L)}{\partial x^2}$, we obtain

$$\frac{\partial^2 \sin(n\pi x/L)}{\partial x^2} = -\frac{n^2\pi^2}{L^2}\sin\frac{n\pi x}{L}$$

or

$$E_n = \frac{n^2 h^2 \pi^2}{8\pi^2 m L^2} \frac{\int_0^L \sin(n\pi x/L)\sin(n\pi x/L)\, dx}{\int_0^L \sin(n\pi x/L)\sin(n\pi x/L)\, dx}$$

Cancellation of all terms common to both the numerator and the denominator affords,

$$E_n = \frac{n^2 h^2}{8mL^2}$$

This is the same result as that which we obtained previously (see equation 2.28).

5. TRAVEL PAST A POTENTIAL BARRIER

Consider the effect of dividing the box in Figure 2–4 in half. This may be done by erecting a thin region at $L/2$ where the potential energy of the electron must be equal to H. Figure 2–6 illustrates the situation. We have a thin wall of height H at $L/2$ and place the particle in the region to the left. Newtonian mechanics predicts that as long as the energy of the particle is less than H, it must remain in the compartment on the left, while, if the particle has total energy greater than H, it is free to travel the full length of the box. This is not so quantum mechanically. The wave mechanical solution to this kind of problem yields the result that the particle may be found on either side of the barrier at $L/2$ even while its energy is less than H. We place the particle on one side with insufficient energy to go over the wall and find that it may actually go through the wall. This is known as the *tunnel effect.* Conversely, it is found that a particle having total energy greater than H may actually be reflected at the wall. The particle approaches the wall with more than sufficient energy to clear it and yet may be turned back. The probability of either of these events occurring depends on the height and width of the barrier and is due entirely to the wave properties of matter. The tunnel effect is found in the alpha decay of radioactive materials. Close to the nucleus, the Coulombic repulsion between the nucleus and the alpha particle is greater than the total energy of the alpha particle, yet these particles are ejected from the nucleus and must pass through the region of high potential.

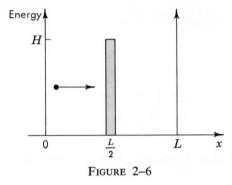

FIGURE 2–6

6. THE HYDROGEN ATOM AND PROBLEMS RELATED TO THE PARTICLE IN A BOX

Various related problems exist, such as the particle in a cubic box, the particle in a rectangular box, and the particle in a circle. The first two of these are the three-dimensional problems, each of which may be separated into 3 one-dimensional problems. Each one-dimensional problem is treated in the manner just described. Recombination of the one-dimensional solutions gives the desired result. Three quantum numbers are required.

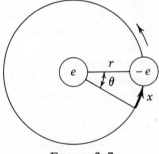

FIGURE 2–7

The particle in a circle is an interesting case because it is similar to the Bohr hydrogen atom. The motion of the electron is restricted to a circle of radius r. The Hamiltonian for the system is $H = E = T + U$ where T is the kinetic energy of the electron, and the potential energy is constant and equal to $-e^2/r$. This may be regarded as a one-dimensional problem where the distance x is measured on the circumference of a circle, $x = r\theta$, and θ is measured in radians. The problem is illustrated in Figure 2–7.

The Schrödinger equation for this case becomes

$$-\frac{h^2}{8\pi^2 m}\frac{\partial^2\psi}{\partial x^2} = (E - U)\psi$$

where

$$U = -\frac{e^2}{r}$$

This differential equation is identical in form with that of the particle in a box and has the same solution

$$\psi = A \sin\frac{2\pi}{h}\sqrt{2m(E - U)}x + B \cos\frac{2\pi}{h}\sqrt{2m(E - U)}x$$

Remember that

$$\frac{1}{\lambda} = \frac{p}{h}$$

which leads to

$$\frac{1}{\lambda} = \frac{\sqrt{2m(E - U)}}{h} \tag{2.30}$$

For a particle moving along a circle of radius r, $x = r\theta$, and

$$\psi = A \sin\frac{2\pi r}{h}\sqrt{2m(E - U)}\theta + B \cos\frac{2\pi r}{h}\sqrt{2m(E - U)}\theta \tag{2.31}$$

It is simpler to make the substitution given in equation (2.30) and work with the equation in this form.

$$\psi = A \sin\frac{2\pi r}{\lambda}\theta + B \cos\frac{2\pi r}{\lambda}\theta \tag{2.32}$$

The eigenfunctions given by equation (2.31) or (2.32) are subject to the restriction previously encountered in the Bohr quantum theory. In order for the electron to travel the same orbit repeatedly, the circumference of the circle must contain an integral number of wavelengths, and it is this condition that quantizes the eigenvalues.

We have

$$2\pi r = n\lambda \qquad n = 0, 1, 2, 3 \cdots$$

Substitution of $n\lambda$ for $2\pi r$ in equation (2.32) yields

$$\psi_n = A \sin n\theta + B \cos n\theta \qquad n = 0, 1, 2, 3 \cdots \qquad (2.33)$$

This is the solution to the problem of a particle moving along a circle of radius r; these eigenfunctions have been illustrated in Figure 1–11 for $n = 1, 2, 3$. Quantum mechanics tells us that ψ exists, and therefore, that a particle exists even when $n = 0$. In that case $\psi = B$. The Bohr theory required that n not be zero (see equation 1.21). The eigenvalues are obtained by comparing equations (2.31) and (2.33).

$$\frac{2\pi r}{h} \sqrt{2m(E - U)} = n \qquad n = 0, 1, 2, 3 \cdots$$

or

$$E_n = \frac{n^2 h^2}{8\pi^2 m r^2} + U$$

$$E_n = \frac{n^2 h^2}{8\pi^2 m r^2} - \frac{e^2}{r} \qquad (2.34)$$

Again, we have quantized the total energy of the system, yet this result is different in many respects from that obtained from the Bohr theory.

The quantization of orbital angular momentum remains for $n\lambda$ still equals $2\pi r$

$$n\lambda = 2\pi r$$

since

$$\lambda = \frac{h}{p}$$

$$\lambda = \frac{h}{mv}$$

then

$$\frac{nh}{mv} = 2\pi r$$

or

$$mvr = \frac{nh}{2\pi}$$

and

$$L = mvr$$

therefore,

$$L = \frac{nh}{2\pi} \qquad n = 0, 1, 2, 3 \cdots$$

The first expression in equation (2.34) is a kinetic energy term. Maintaining r constant, and increasing n, keeps the electron in the same orbit with increased kinetic energy.

The particle in a circle is not the true hydrogen atom. In reality the motion of the electron is unrestricted and a three-dimensional equation is required. The Schrödinger equation becomes

$$H\psi = E\psi$$

or

$$-\frac{h^2}{8\pi^2 m} \left[\frac{\partial^2 \psi}{\partial x^2} + \frac{\partial^2 \psi}{\partial y^2} + \frac{\partial^2 \psi}{\partial z^2} \right] - \frac{e^2}{r} \psi = E\psi$$

This differential equation is solved most easily by transforming to spherical coordinates (see Figure 2–8).

In those cases where a solution is effected most easily by using some other coordinate system, it is first necessary to set up the Schrödinger equation for the problem in Cartesian coordinates (x, y, z) and subsequently make the transformation. For the hydrogen atom it is the fact that the potential energy is a function of the distance r that makes the transformation to spherical coordinates necessary. The solution is lengthy. A three-dimensional problem requires the introduction of three quantum numbers (n, l, and m). Furthermore, the solution has physical significance only if certain restrictions are placed on these quantum numbers. Accordingly, the principal quantum number n can take on the possible values 1, 2, 3, and so forth, while for a given n, the angular momentum quantum number l may take on

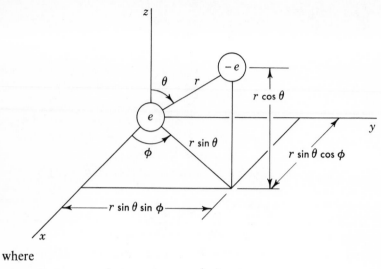

where

$$x = r \sin \theta \cos \phi$$

$$y = r \sin \theta \sin \phi$$

$$z = r \cos \theta$$

FIGURE 2–8

the integral values 0, 1, 2, 3 $\cdots$, $n - 1$. This quantum number is a measure of the orbital angular momentum of the electron. The magnetic quantum number m is restricted to those integers between $-l$ and $+l$, that is, $-l, \cdots, -2, -1, 0, +1, +2, \ldots, +l$. We present the results for the first three eigenfunctions.

	n	l	m	ψ
$1s$	1	0	0	$\dfrac{1}{\sqrt{\pi}} \left(\dfrac{1}{a_o}\right)^{3/2} e^{-(r/a_o)}$
$2s$	2	0	0	$\dfrac{1}{4\sqrt{2\pi}} \left(\dfrac{1}{a_o}\right)^{3/2} \left(2 - \dfrac{r}{a_o}\right) e^{-(r/2a_o)}$
$2p_z$	2	1	0	$\dfrac{1}{4\sqrt{2\pi}} \left(\dfrac{1}{a_o}\right)^{3/2} \left(\dfrac{r}{a_o}\right) e^{-(r/2a_o)} \cos \theta$†

† In equation (2.19) we have replaced $r \cos \theta$ by z.

where

$$a_o = \frac{h^2}{4\pi^2 m e^2}$$

The Schrödinger equation does not predict the existence of electronic spin and does not give rise to a spin quantum number. However, relativistic quantum mechanics does predict the existence of electronic spin and requires the introduction of a spin quantum number s. In a nonrelativistic treatment spin is taken into account by means of the Pauli exclusion principle.

7. THE AUFBAU PRINCIPLE AND THE PERIODIC TABLE

The one-electron problem such as the hydrogen atom and the helium plus ion, He^+, can be solved exactly. The situation is not so simple in the many electron case. The Hamiltonian for the helium atom is

$$H = \frac{p_1^2}{2m} + \frac{p_2^2}{2m} - \frac{2e^2}{r_1} - \frac{2e^2}{r_2} + \frac{e^2}{r_{12}}$$

The Schrödinger equation for this system becomes

$$H\psi = E\psi$$

$$-\frac{h^2}{8\pi^2 m}\left[\frac{\partial^2\psi}{\partial x_1^2} + \frac{\partial^2\psi}{\partial y_1^2} + \frac{\partial^2\psi}{\partial z_1^2}\right] - \frac{h^2}{8\pi^2 m}\left[\frac{\partial^2\psi}{\partial x_2^2} + \frac{\partial^2\psi}{\partial y_2^2} + \frac{\partial^2\psi}{\partial z_2^2}\right]$$
$$-\frac{2e^2}{r_1}\psi - \frac{2e^2}{r_2}\psi + \frac{e^2}{r_{12}}\psi = E\psi \qquad (2.35)$$

where the subscripts 1 and 2 refer to electrons 1 and 2. Our equation has become involved very quickly, yet a good approximate solution to this equation can be obtained. First assume that the electrons are noninteracting, that there is no repulsion between electrons. The term e^2/r_{12} is neglected in the Hamiltonian for the time being. Now, the Schrödinger equation corresponding to this simplified Hamiltonian is composed of two hydrogen-like expressions which can be solved. One comes up with the conclusion that in the ground state both electrons may occupy the same orbital. Since in the absence of interelectronic repulsion the two expressions on the left side of equation (2.35) are identical, this is not unexpected. Having solved the Schrödinger equation for two independently moving electrons, the expression e^2/r_{12} is considered in the Hamiltonian and one calculates, in effect, the average potential energy of repulsion between two electrons occupying the same orbital.

	IA	IIA											IIIA	IVA	VA	VIA	VIIA	0
	1H 1																	2He 2
	3Li 2 1	4Be 2 2											5B 2 3	6C 2 4	7N 2 5	8O 2 6	9F 2 7	10Ne 2 8
	11Na 2 8 1	12Mg 2 8 2											13Al 2 8 3	14Si 2 8 4	15P 2 8 5	16S 2 8 6	17Cl 2 8 7	18A 2 8 8
	19K 2 8 8 1	20Ca 2 8 8 2	21Sc 2 8 9 2	22Ti 2 8 10 2	23V 2 8 11 2	24Cr 2 8 13 1	25Mn 2 8 13 2	26Fe 2 8 14 2	27Co 2 8 15 2	28Ni 2 8 16 2	29Cu 2 8 18 1	30Zn 2 8 18 2	31Ga 2 8 18 3	32Ge 2 8 18 4	33As 2 8 18 5	34Se 2 8 18 6	35Br 2 8 18 7	36Kr 2 8 18 8
	37Rb 2 8 18 8 1	38Sr 2 8 18 8 2	39Y 2 8 18 9 2	40Zr 2 8 18 10 2	41Nb 2 8 18 12 1	42Mo 2 8 18 13 1	43Tc 2 8 18 13 2	44Ru 2 8 18 15 1	45Rh 2 8 18 16 1	46Pd 2 8 18 18	47Ag 2 8 18 18 1	48Cd 2 8 18 18 2	49In 2 8 18 18 3	50Sn 2 8 18 18 4	51Sb 2 8 18 18 5	52Te 2 8 18 18 6	53I 2 8 18 18 7	54Xe 2 8 18 18 8
	55Cs 2 8 18 18 8 1	56Ba 2 8 18 18 8 2	57-71*	72Hf 2 8 18 32 10 2	73Ta 2 8 18 32 11 2	74W 2 8 18 32 12 2	75Re 2 8 18 32 13 2	76Os 2 8 18 32 14 2	77Ir 2 8 18 32 15 2	78Pt 2 8 18 32 17 1	79Au 2 8 18 32 18 1	80Hg 2 8 18 32 18 2	81Tl 2 8 18 32 18 3	82Pb 2 8 18 32 18 4	83Bi 2 8 18 32 18 5	84Po 2 8 18 32 18 6	85At 2 8 18 32 18 7	86Rn 2 8 18 32 18 8

Main table (period 7, beginning):

Shell	87Fr	88Ra	89–103**
	2	2	
	8	8	
	18	18	
	32	32	
	18	18	
	8	8	
	1	2	

*Lanthanides (Rare Earths)

Shell	57La	58Ce	59Pr	60Nd	61Pm	62Sm	63Eu	64Gd	65Tb	66Dy	67Ho	68Er	69Tm	70Yb	71Lu
	2	2	2	2	2	2	2	2	2	2	2	2	2	2	2
	8	8	8	8	8	8	8	8	8	8	8	8	8	8	8
	18	18	18	18	18	18	18	18	18	18	18	18	18	18	18
	18	20	21	22	23	24	25	25	26	27	28	29	31	32	32
	9	8	8	8	8	8	8	9	9	9	9	9	8	8	9
	2	2	2	2	2	2	2	2	2	2	2	2	2	2	2

**Actinides

Shell	89Ac	90Th	91Pa	92U	93Np	94Pu	95Am	96Cm	97Bk	98Cf	99Es	100Fm	101Md	102No	103Lw
	2	2	2	2	2	2	2	2	2	2	?	?	?	?	?
	8	8	8	8	8	8	8	8	8	8					
	18	18	18	18	18	18	18	18	18	18					
	32	32	32	32	32	32	32	32	32	32					
	18	18	20	21	22	24	25	25	26	27					
	9	10	9	9	9	8	8	9	9	9					
	2	2	2	2	2	2	2	2	2	2					

FIGURE 2–9 THE PERIODIC TABLE AND THE GROUND STATE ELECTRONIC CONFIGURATIONS OF THE ELEMENTS

In this way the Schrödinger equation is solved. This technique is an example of perturbation theory where the term e^2/r_{12} is considered to be a perturbation to the system of two independent electrons. This method gives good results for $_2$He, yet as the system becomes more complicated, the Schrödinger equation becomes increasingly difficult to solve. In those cases where the atoms contain numerous electrons the situation is quite complicated and still more approximate solutions are necessary.

The Hamiltonian for a many-electron system includes terms for the interelectronic repulsion, and as we saw in the treatment of the helium atom, it is these terms that render impossible an exact solution to the Schrödinger equation. Again a solution to the problem may be effected by assuming that the electrons are noninteracting. However, since there are now many terms representing repulsion between the electrons, these terms may no longer be neglected in the Hamiltonian. Just as in the case of the helium atom, the total Hamiltonian for the system is separated into its one-electron components. Each one-electron Hamiltonian now contains a term for the kinetic energy of that electron, a term representing the potential energy of attraction of that electron for the nucleus, and a term that represents the average potential energy of repulsion between that electron and all other electrons present in the system. This last term must be approximated. The one-electron Schrödinger equation corresponding to this Hamiltonian is now solved. Combination of all these one-electron solutions gives the solution for the entire system. On the basis of this solution a better approximation can be made for the interelectronic repulsion term, and using this better approximation, the Schrödinger equation for the one electron is solved again. Thus, by a series of successive approximations we can obtain a reasonably correct solution to the problem. In the treatment just described, use must be made of the Pauli exclusion principle, which states that no more than two electrons may occupy the same orbital and that these two must be of opposite spin. If the system contains more than two electrons, this principle prevents all of them from occupying the same orbital.

If we are only interested in the ground state electronic configuration of an atom, it is not necessary to carry out a rigorous calculation. The permitted eigenfunctions for an electron are $1s$, $2s$, and so forth. Having found the allowed orbitals, we next arrange them in order of increasing energy. Then, beginning with the orbital of lowest energy, we place the available electrons into these orbitals in a manner that is consistent with the Pauli exclusion principle. In proceeding from one element to the next, the energy sequence of the orbitals remains essentially unaltered. As the elements increase in atomic number, we simply add electrons to those available orbitals having the lowest energy. This procedure is called the Aufbau principle, and if we arrange in columns those elements having similar electronic configurations, we obtain the periodic table (see Figure 2–9).

PROBLEMS

1. What are the normalized eigenfunctions for a particle confined to a box extending along the x axis from $-L/2$ to $L/2$?

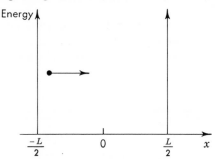

2. What is the Schrödinger equation in polar coordinates (r, θ) for a particle traveling in a circle of radius r?
3. Show the orthogonality of $\psi_0(n = 0)$ and $\psi_1(n = 1)$ for the particle in a circle (see equation 2.33). The integration is over all values of θ. $0 \leq \theta \leq 2\pi$.
4. The following identities are known as Euler's identities,[2]

$$e^{i\theta} = \cos \theta + i \sin \theta$$

$$e^{-i\theta} = \cos \theta - i \sin \theta$$

where

$$i = \sqrt{-1}$$

Restate equation (2.2) in terms of exponentials.

---

[2] From the series expansions of these functions:

$$e^z = 1 + z + \frac{z^2}{2!} + \frac{z^3}{3!}$$

$$\sin z = z - \frac{z^3}{3!} + \frac{z^5}{5!} - \frac{z^7}{7!}$$

$$\cos z = 1 - \frac{z^2}{2!} + \frac{z^4}{4!} - \frac{z^6}{6!}$$

5. How do you think the following affect the probability of a particle's passing through a potential barrier ("tunnel effect")?

   (a) Keeping the barrier the same but increasing the energy of the particle.

   (b) Keeping the energy of the particle constant while increasing the height of the barrier.

   (c) Maintaining the energy of the particle while increasing the width of the barrier.

6. Set up the Schrödinger equation for the helium plus ion, He^+.

7. Set up the Schrödinger equation for $_3Li$.

Chapter Three

THE HÜCKEL MOLECULAR-ORBITAL THEORY

1. PROPERTIES OF MOLECULAR ORBITALS

The basic assumption of the molecular-orbital method is that an eigenfunction can be used to represent an electron in a molecule just as an electron in an atom is described by a similar function. The chief difference is that the molecular electron is simultaneously in the electrostatic field of several nuclei. Inasmuch as the situation is far more complicated, molecular problems are not solved so readily as are the atomic situations. In fact, an exact solution to the Schrödinger equation is not possible in these more difficult cases, so the exact eigenfunctions and eigenvalues are not known. What is usually done is to select an eigenfunction arbitrarily and to assume that this is the solution to the Schrödinger equation. Then, using this function, it is possible to obtain eigenvalues. The accuracy of this technique naturally depends upon the choice of eigenfunctions. A choice that describes reasonably well the probable positions of a molecular electron leads to eigenvalues that are in good agreement with experimental results. Once a method for generating molecular orbitals has been shown to work, it is employed even in cases where experimental verification is not possible. The molecular orbitals that serve as eigenfunctions in the Hückel method obey all the rules of atomic orbitals. The Aufbau principle that is employed in the development of the periodic table is followed exactly. The energy of an electron in the various molecular orbitals is first calculated, and just as in the case of atomic orbitals, each accommodates two electrons of opposite spin. In the ground state the orbitals are filled by starting with that of lowest energy and working to higher energies. When dealing with four electrons, two are placed in the most stable and two in the next most stable molecular orbital. Excitation involves the transition of an electron from one orbital to another of higher energy. In the case of degenerate orbitals, one electron with parallel spin goes into each until all orbitals are half filled. If any electrons remain, these are used to fill the degenerate orbitals. Atomic oxygen, $_8O$, serves as an example.

$$1s \quad 2s \quad 2p_x \quad 2p_y \quad 2p_z \quad 3s \quad 3p_x \quad 3p_y \quad 3p_z$$
$$\uparrow\downarrow \quad \uparrow\downarrow \quad \uparrow\downarrow \quad \uparrow \quad \uparrow$$

FIGURE 3–1   PLACING ELECTRONS IN
THE ATOMIC ORBITALS OF OXYGEN

First, the energy of an electron in the various orbitals is calculated (see Figure 3–1). The result is, $1s$ then $2s$, next $2p_x$, $2p_y$, and $2p_z$, which are degenerate, followed by $3s$, and $3p_x$, $3p_y$, and $3p_z$, which are degenerate, and so forth. Now, there are eight electrons — two go into the $1s$ level, two in the $2s$, and next, one each in the $2p_x$, $2p_y$, and $2p_z$. The last electron is placed back in the $2p_x$, and we have used up the eight electrons. This same procedure is employed in the Hückel theory.

Perhaps the most serious drawback of the Hückel theory occurs with this Aufbau procedure. The energy associated with the various orbitals is assumed to remain unaltered even in the presence of other electrons. Consider two electrons in an orbital, the energy of the two is supposedly twice that of the singly occupied orbital. We have neglected interelectronic repulsion. More elaborate theories correct for this. The Hückel theory does not do so explicitly.

2. THE LINEAR-COMBINATION-OF-ATOMIC-ORBITALS METHOD

Consider any two functions x_1 and x_2. A sum of the form

$$a_1x_1 + a_2x_2$$

where a_1 and a_2 are constants is called a *linear combination* of x_1 and x_2. Analogously, in the hydrogen molecule the sigma bond is a molecular orbital that is expressed as a linear combination of the two $1s$ atomic orbitals, one from each hydrogen atom.

$$H_1—H_2$$
$$\uparrow$$
$$s-s$$

$$\psi_{HH} = a_1s_1 + a_2s_2$$

where the subscripts 1 and 2 refer to the atoms. Two entire atomic orbitals are not required to construct one molecular orbital. Merely a fraction of each atomic orbital is needed. The coefficient a_1 is related to the fraction of atomic orbital s_1 used in the construction of the molecular orbital. A similar interpretation may be given to a_2. It is related to the fraction of s_2 utilized. The values of a_1 and a_2 will always be less than unity. This method is the usual one employed for the construction of molecular orbitals. They are generated from atomic orbitals. Such an approach to molecular problems is called the linear-combination-of-atomic-orbitals method,[1] and in fact, this is the picture that one has of chemical bonds. The bonds holding the atoms together in a molecule are molecular eigenfunctions composed of atomic eigenfunctions.

In those cases where inner-shell electrons are present, it is assumed that these make no contribution to bond formation, that is, bonding involves only valence electrons. Therefore, in a diatomic molecule such as hydrogen chloride the molecular eigenfunction is formed as a linear combination involving the $1s$ atomic eigenfunction of hydrogen and the $3p$ atomic eigenfunction of chlorine. All other electrons are assumed to occupy the same orbitals in the molecule that they occupy in the chlorine atom.

$$\text{H}{-}\text{Cl}$$
$$\uparrow$$
$$s - p$$

$$\psi_{\text{HCl}} = a_1 s + a_2 p$$

In the ethane molecule each sigma bond may be treated separately. A carbon-hydrogen bond is then a molecular orbital composed of the $1s$ atomic orbital of hydrogen and an sp^3 atomic orbital of carbon, while the constituents of the carbon-carbon bond are both sp^3 orbitals.

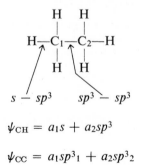

$$\psi_{\text{CH}} = a_1 s + a_2 sp^3$$

$$\psi_{\text{CC}} = a_1 sp^3{}_1 + a_2 sp^3{}_2$$

[1] R. S. Mulliken, *J. Chem. Phys.*, **3**, 375 (1935).

In each case the values of a_1 and a_2 are related to the fractions of atomic orbitals used.

In the molecular-orbital treatment of ethylene and for most other alkenes one makes the further assumption that there is no interaction between σ and π electrons. Consequently, the following eigenfunctions are present.

$$\psi_{CH} \quad = a_1 s \quad\; + a_2 sp^2$$

$$\psi_{CC}(\sigma) = a_1 sp^2{}_1 + a_2 sp^2{}_2$$

$$\psi_{CC}(\pi) = a_1 p_1 \quad + a_2 p_2$$

In butadiene there are nine σ-bonds containing 18 electrons, and 4 electrons that must be accommodated in π-molecular orbitals. A π-molecular orbital contains 2 electrons and encompasses all four carbon atoms. Such an orbital is then a linear combination of p_z atomic orbitals, one from each of these carbon atoms.

$$\psi = a_1 p_1 + a_2 p_2 + a_3 p_3 + a_4 p_4$$

The 4 π-electrons present in butadiene are placed in two different π-bond molecular orbitals. Each one of these two molecular orbitals is formed as a linear combination of p_z atomic orbitals; however, the values of a_1, a_2, a_3 and a_4 differ as does their energy. Four π-electrons are accommodated in two molecular orbitals, each having the form

$$\psi = a_1 p_1 + a_2 p_2 + a_3 p_3 + a_4 p_4$$

For benzene a π-bond eigenfunction can be written as:

$$\psi = a_1 p_1 + a_2 p_2 + a_3 p_3 + a_4 p_4 + a_5 p_5 + a_6 p_6$$

The 6 π-electrons are placed in three molecular orbitals of this type.

In the case of cyclobutadiene the π orbitals again include four atoms:

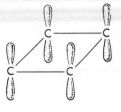

and

$$\psi = a_1 p_1 + a_2 p_2 + a_3 p_3 + a_4 p_4$$

In addition, there are certain radicals and ions that are of interest such as the allyl system

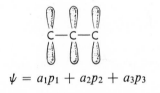

$$\psi = a_1 p_1 + a_2 p_2 + a_3 p_3$$

the cyclopropenyl system

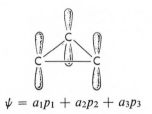

$$\psi = a_1 p_1 + a_2 p_2 + a_3 p_3$$

and the cyclopentadienyl system.

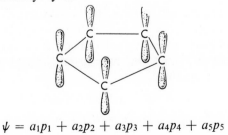

$$\psi = a_1 p_1 + a_2 p_2 + a_3 p_3 + a_4 p_4 + a_5 p_5$$

3. PARAMETERS IN THE HÜCKEL MOLECULAR-ORBITAL THEORY

The Hückel molecular-orbital theory is developed in terms of two parameters that are evaluated experimentally. Imagine a molecule of ethylene prior to the formation of the π bond.

The electron is then in one of the p atomic orbitals with energy E. If it is in p_1, then the Schrödinger equation for this electron becomes:

$$Hp_1 = Ep_1 \quad \text{(see equation 2.16)}$$

Multiplying both sides by p_1 and integrating,

$$\int p_1 Hp_1 \, dv = \int p_1 Ep_1 \, dv$$

Since E is a number, it can be taken out from under the integral sign and

$$\int p_1 Hp_1 \, dv = E \int p_1 p_1 \, dv$$

and since the p orbitals are normalized,

$$\int p_1 p_1 \, dv = 1$$

Therefore,

$$\int p_1 Hp_1 \, dv = E \tag{3.1}$$

The expression on the left of equation (3.1) is the Coulomb integral. It represents the energy of an electron in a $2p$ atomic orbital of carbon. The integral, a parameter to be evaluated, is negative since the electron is attracted to the nucleus. This Coulomb integral is designated either by the symbol H_{11} or merely by alpha, α.

$$\int p_1 Hp_1 \, dv = H_{11} = \alpha$$

Similarly, the term

$$\int p_2 H p_2 \, dv$$

represents the energy of an electron in atomic orbital p_2. This has the same value and is designated as H_{22} or α.

$$\int p_2 H p_2 \, dv = H_{22} = \alpha$$

The other parameter β represents the energy of an electron when it is between carbon atoms 1 and 2. This is also a negative quantity and is called the resonance integral.

$$\int p_1 H p_2 \, dv = H_{12} = \beta \qquad (3.2)$$

$$\int p_2 H p_1 \, dv = H_{21} = \beta$$

Now consider one of the electrons in the π bond of ethylene. We are interested in the energy of this electron and its probable location within the molecule. This energy is expressed in terms of the parameters α and β. The electron in the molecular orbital,

$$\psi = a_1 p_1 + a_2 p_2$$

which represents the π bond of ethylene, has energy

$$E = \alpha + \beta$$

where E is negative.

The standard to which the stability of all molecular orbitals is compared is α (see Figure 3–2). If an electron in a molecular orbital ψ is more stable than an electron in a p atomic orbital, then ψ is a bonding molecular orbital. For example, if the energy of an electron associated with ψ is $\alpha + \beta$, then ψ is bonding. Whereas, if an electron in ψ is less stable than an electron in a p atomic orbital, ψ is antibonding. This would be the case if the energy associated with ψ is $\alpha - \beta$. Remember that the more negative its energy, the more stable is the electron and β is itself negative. If $E = \alpha$, then ψ is non-bonding.

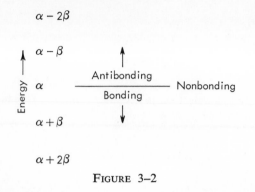

FIGURE 3–2

Energy differences between orbitals are expressed in terms of β, and it is this parameter that is the more significant. Numerical evaluation depends upon the technique employed and the assumptions involved. Consider the thermodynamic evaluation of β. The following heats of hydrogenation have been measured (see Figure 3–3).

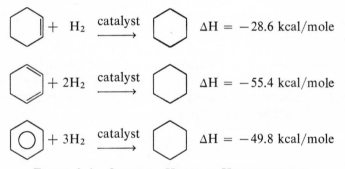

FIGURE 3–3   OBSERVED HEATS OF HYDROGENATION

Cyclohexadiene with two double bonds might be expected to exhibit a heat of hydrogenation equal to twice that of cyclohexene and benzene a value three times that of cyclohexene.

$$2 \times -28.6 = -57.2 \text{ kcal/mole}$$

$$3 \times -28.6 = -85.8 \text{ kcal/mole}$$

The observed values are less than this. The diene is 1.8 kcal/mole more stable than expected while benzene is 36.0 kcal/mole more stable.

$$57.2 - 55.4 = 1.8 \text{ kcal/mole}$$

$$85.8 - 49.8 = 36.0 \text{ kcal/mole}$$

This unexpected stability is usually assumed to be equal to the resonance energy of these compounds. The results are depicted in Figure 3–4. The dotted lines represent hypothetical values.

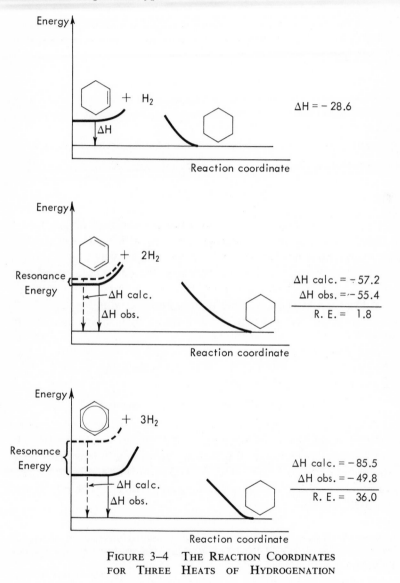

FIGURE 3–4   THE REACTION COORDINATES
FOR   THREE   HEATS   OF   HYDROGENATION

The resonance energy of a compound is usually considered to be the energy difference between the most stable classical structure and the compound, itself.[2] Resonance energies are always positive. While *resonance energy* is valence-bond terminology, this concept is more firmly entrenched and more familiar than the molecular-orbital idea of delocalization energy. The two are completely equivalent.

We shall carry out the Hückel molecular-orbital calculation for benzene later in the chapter and shall find it to have a resonance energy equal to -2β. If we equate,

$$-2\beta = 36$$

$$\beta = -18 \text{ kcal/mole} \qquad (3.3)$$

We have obtained one possible value of β.

The length of the carbon-carbon double bond in cyclohexene is approximately equal to 1.33 A, and the heat of hydrogenation is -28.6 kcal/mole.

A compound having three such localized double bonds of length 1.33 A is calculated to have a heat of hydrogenation equal to -85.8 kcal/mole. But this compound is not benzene. All carbon-carbon distances in benzene are equivalent and equal to 1.39 A. Whereas, the compound under consideration is a cyclohexatriene which has three single bonds, approximately 1.50 A in length, and three isolated double bonds having length 1.33 A. We have calculated that benzene is more stable than cyclohexatriene by 36 kcal/mole.

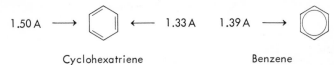

Cyclohexatriene   Benzene

A modified cyclohexatriene that has all carbon-carbon bond distances equal to 1.39 A, the value in benzene, is still less stable. Decreasing the length of the single bonds and lengthening the double bonds destabilizes the compound by 27 kcal/mole.[3] The vertical resonance energy of benzene is defined as the difference between the energy of this compound and benzene, itself.[4]

---

[2] L. Pauling, *The Nature of the Chemical Bond*, Cornell University Press, Ithaca, N.Y., 1939, p.12; see also G. W. Wheland, *Resonance in Organic Chemistry*, Wiley, New York, N.Y., 1955, p. 75.

[3] C. A. Coulson and S. L. Altmann, *Trans. Faraday Soc.*, **48**, 293 (1952).

[4] G. W. Wheland, *Resonance in Organic Chemistry*, Wiley, New York, N.Y., 1955, p. 129. See also A. Streitwieser, Jr., *Molecular Orbital Theory for Organic Chemists*, Wiley, New York, N. Y., 1961, p. 245.

Vertical Resonance Energy $= 36 + 27$

$$= 63 \text{ kcal/mole}$$

This result is diagrammatically illustrated in Figure 3–5.

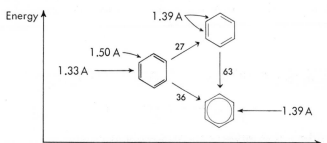

FIGURE 3–5 THE VERTICAL RESONANCE ENERGY OF BENZENE

Equating the molecular-orbital resonance energy -2β to the vertical resonance energy,

$$-2\beta = 63$$

$$\beta = -32 \text{ kcal/mole} \qquad (3.4)$$

Changing the definition of resonance energy leads to a different value for β. Still another value comes from a consideration of the excitation energies of certain alkenes. We shall consider the excitation energy as the energy required to promote an electron from the highest occupied molecular orbital to the lowest energy unoccupied molecular orbital (see Figure 3–6).

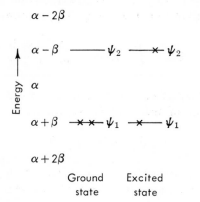

FIGURE 3–6 THE ENERGY OF THE GROUND STATE AND FIRST EXCITED STATE FOR THE TWO π – ELECTRONS IN ETHYLENE

In the ground state of ethylene both π electrons are in a bonding molecular orbital of energy $\alpha + \beta$. Excitation involves the transfer of one electron from this orbital to an antibonding orbital of energy $\alpha - \beta$. Before excitation, there are two electrons each with energy $\alpha + \beta$, and the energy of the system is $2\alpha + 2\beta$. Afterwards, one electron still has energy $\alpha + \beta$ while the energy of the other is now $\alpha - \beta$. The excitation energy is:

$$\alpha + \beta \quad + \quad \alpha - \beta \quad - (2\alpha + 2\beta) = -2\beta$$

Experimental determination of β from this type of procedure yields:

$$\beta = -60 \text{ kcal/mole} \tag{3.5}$$

a value nowhere near either of the two previous results.

Considering the approximations which are made, it is not too surprising that β varies. We must choose a value consistent with the work being done.

In addition to α and β, the Hückel theory involves integrals of the type,

$$S_{11} = \int p_1 p_1 \, dv$$

$$S_{12} = \int p_1 p_2 \, dv$$

$$S_{13} = \int p_1 p_3 \, dv$$

where p_1, p_2, and p_3 are the p_z orbitals on carbon atoms 1, 2, and 3 of some compound. We shall assume that these form an orthonormal set, that is,

$$S_{AB} = \int p_A p_B \, dv = \begin{cases} 1 & A = B \\ 0 & A \neq B \end{cases} \tag{3.6}$$

All orbitals are normalized, and the integrals S_{11}, S_{22}, or in general S_{AA}, certainly have a value of unity, yet the assumption

$$S_{AB} = 0 \quad A \neq B$$

is not strictly correct. The orbitals in question are all p_z orbitals, and S_{AB}, the overlap integral, is a measure of the overlap between p_A and p_B. If carbon atoms A and B are widely separated, then no significant overlap occurs and S_{AB} can be set equal to zero. However, if appreciable overlap between

p_A and p_B exists, then S_{AB} is not zero, and in fact, one usually considers π-bond formation to result from such orbital overlap. This simplification is corrected by adjusting β which also indicates π-bond formation. The values of β obtained previously assume equation (3.6) to be correct.

The molecular orbital for one of the π electrons in butadiene can be expressed as:

$$\psi = a_1 p_1 + a_2 p_2 + a_3 p_3 + a_4 p_4$$

Determination of the energy of an electron occupying this orbital involves in addition to terms such as:

$$H_{11} = \int p_1 H p_1 \, dv$$

$$H_{22} = \int p_2 H p_2 \, dv$$

$$H_{33} = \int p_3 H p_3 \, dv$$

and

$$H_{44} = \int p_4 H p_4 \, dv$$

which are all equal to α, expressions like

$$H_{12} = \int p_1 H p_2 \, dv$$

$$H_{31} = \int p_3 H p_1 \, dv$$

$$H_{32} = \int p_3 H p_2 \, dv$$

$$H_{14} = \int p_1 H p_4 \, dv \tag{3.7}$$

The value of these mixed integrals, (3.7), is directly proportional to the degree of overlap between the p orbitals in question. When the orbitals are on adjacent carbon atoms, their value is β, for example,

$$H_{12} = H_{32} = \beta$$

It may appear inconsistent to set $H_{12} = \beta$ and $S_{12} = 0$, yet this considerably simplifies the mathematics, and as was mentioned, β may be modified to take this into account. If the orbitals are far apart, overlap is negligible, and the integrals can be set equal to zero. This is the situation when the orbitals are on nonadjacent atoms.

$$H_{31} = H_{14} = 0$$

Thus, the terms $H_{AB} = \int p_A H p_B \, dv$ are set equal to β if carbon atoms A and B are adjacent (bonded) and equal to zero if A and B are not adjacent.

4. DETERMINANTS

An expression of the form

$$\begin{vmatrix} a & b \\ c & d \end{vmatrix}$$

is called a determinant of the second order, where the four letters a, b, c, d are the elements. The elements in a horizontal line comprise a row and the elements in a vertical line a column of the determinant. Evaluation of the second-order determinant yields:

$$\begin{vmatrix} a & b \\ c & d \end{vmatrix} = ad - bc$$

Higher-order determinants are expanded in terms of elements and cofactors. For example, we define a third-order determinant by the equation,

$$\begin{vmatrix} a & b & c \\ d & e & f \\ g & h & i \end{vmatrix} = a \cdot \begin{vmatrix} e & f \\ h & i \end{vmatrix} - b \cdot \begin{vmatrix} d & f \\ g & i \end{vmatrix} + c \cdot \begin{vmatrix} d & e \\ g & h \end{vmatrix} \tag{3.8}$$

$$= a(ei - fh) - b(di - fg) + c(dh - eg)$$

$$= aei - afh - bdi + bfg + cdh - ceg$$

Notice the alternating $+$ and $-$ signs in expression (3.8). The second-order determinant that multiplies each element in (3.8) is obtained from the third-order determinant by leaving out that row and column to which the element belongs.

$$\begin{vmatrix} a & b & c \\ d & e & f \\ g & h & i \end{vmatrix} \qquad \begin{vmatrix} a & b & c \\ d & e & f \\ g & h & i \end{vmatrix} \qquad \begin{vmatrix} a & b & c \\ d & e & f \\ g & h & i \end{vmatrix}$$

A fourth-order determinant can be expanded in terms of lower-order determinants in a like manner.

$$
\begin{vmatrix} a & b & c & d \\ e & f & g & h \\ i & j & k & l \\ m & n & o & p \end{vmatrix} = a \begin{vmatrix} f & g & h \\ j & k & l \\ n & o & p \end{vmatrix} - b \begin{vmatrix} e & g & h \\ i & k & l \\ m & o & p \end{vmatrix} +
$$

$$
c \begin{vmatrix} e & f & h \\ i & j & l \\ m & n & p \end{vmatrix} - d \begin{vmatrix} e & f & g \\ i & j & k \\ m & n & o \end{vmatrix}
$$

The expression on the right may be expanded further using the *development* indicated previously. A determinant of the fifth order is developed in an analogous fashion.

$$
\begin{vmatrix} a & b & c & d & e \\ f & g & h & i & j \\ k & l & m & n & o \\ p & q & r & s & t \\ u & v & w & x & y \end{vmatrix} = a \begin{vmatrix} g & h & i & j \\ l & m & n & o \\ q & r & s & t \\ v & w & x & y \end{vmatrix} -
$$

$$
b \begin{vmatrix} f & h & i & j \\ k & m & n & o \\ p & r & s & t \\ u & w & x & y \end{vmatrix} + c \begin{vmatrix} f & g & i & j \\ k & l & n & o \\ p & q & s & t \\ u & v & x & y \end{vmatrix} -
$$

$$
d \begin{vmatrix} f & g & h & j \\ k & l & m & o \\ p & q & r & t \\ u & v & w & y \end{vmatrix} + e \begin{vmatrix} f & g & h & i \\ k & l & m & n \\ p & q & r & s \\ u & v & w & x \end{vmatrix}
$$

4.1. THEOREM CONCERNING DETERMINANTS   Multiplication of all the elements in any one row or column by a constant is equivalent to multiplying the entire determinant by that constant.

$$
a \begin{vmatrix} X_{11} & X_{12} \\ X_{21} & X_{22} \end{vmatrix} = \begin{vmatrix} aX_{11} & X_{12} \\ aX_{21} & X_{22} \end{vmatrix} \tag{3.9}
$$

The proof of this statement is obtained upon evaluation of the determinants in question and is illustrated for one of second order. Evaluation of both sides of equation (3.9) gives:

$$a(X_{11}X_{22} - X_{12}X_{21}) = aX_{11}X_{22} - aX_{12}X_{21}$$

or

$$aX_{11}X_{22} - aX_{12}X_{21} = aX_{11}X_{22} - aX_{12}X_{21}$$

Generalizing this result to a determinant of order n,

$$a \begin{vmatrix} X_{11} & X_{12} & X_{13} & \cdots & X_{1n} \\ X_{21} & X_{22} & X_{23} & \cdots & X_{2n} \\ \cdot & \cdot & \cdot & \cdots & \cdot \\ \cdot & \cdot & \cdot & \cdots & \cdot \\ X_{n1} & X_{n2} & X_{n3} & \cdots & X_{nn} \end{vmatrix} = \begin{vmatrix} aX_{11} & X_{12} & X_{13} & \cdots & X_{1n} \\ aX_{21} & X_{22} & X_{23} & \cdots & X_{2n} \\ \cdot & \cdot & \cdot & \cdots & \cdot \\ \cdot & \cdot & \cdot & \cdots & \cdot \\ aX_{n1} & X_{n2} & X_{n3} & \cdots & X_{nn} \end{vmatrix} \qquad (3.10)$$

Now a set of linear equations can be written in determinant form. For example, the following system of three homogeneous linear equations can be written as a single equation involving a third-order determinant where a, b, c are constants.[5]

$$aX_{11} + bX_{12} + cX_{13} = 0$$

$$aX_{21} + bX_{22} + cX_{23} = 0$$

$$aX_{31} + bX_{32} + cX_{33} = 0$$

$$\begin{vmatrix} aX_{11} & bX_{12} & cX_{13} \\ aX_{21} & bX_{22} & cX_{23} \\ aX_{31} & bX_{32} & cX_{33} \end{vmatrix} = 0$$

Since the entire first column is multiplied by a, this factor can be placed before the determinant.

$$\begin{vmatrix} aX_{11} & bX_{12} & cX_{13} \\ aX_{21} & bX_{22} & cX_{23} \\ aX_{31} & bX_{32} & cX_{33} \end{vmatrix} = a \begin{vmatrix} X_{11} & bX_{12} & cX_{13} \\ X_{21} & bX_{22} & cX_{23} \\ X_{31} & bX_{32} & cX_{33} \end{vmatrix} = 0$$

---

[5] The terms a, b, c have been introduced into the determinant. The only mathematical requirement for a nontrivial solution to these equations to exist is that the rank of the matrix $\begin{pmatrix} X_{11} & X_{12} & X_{13} \\ X_{21} & X_{22} & X_{23} \\ X_{31} & X_{32} & X_{33} \end{pmatrix}$ be either 1 or 2.

Similarly,

$$\begin{vmatrix} aX_{11} & bX_{12} & cX_{13} \\ aX_{21} & bX_{22} & cX_{23} \\ aX_{31} & bX_{32} & cX_{33} \end{vmatrix} = a \cdot b \cdot c \begin{vmatrix} X_{11} & X_{12} & X_{13} \\ X_{21} & X_{22} & X_{23} \\ X_{31} & X_{32} & X_{33} \end{vmatrix} = 0 \quad (3.11)$$

Now a, b, and c in expression (3.11) cannot be equal to zero since they are constants. Therefore, for expression (3.11) to hold, the determinant must equal zero.

$$\begin{vmatrix} X_{11} & X_{12} & X_{13} \\ X_{21} & X_{22} & X_{23} \\ X_{31} & X_{32} & X_{33} \end{vmatrix} = 0 \qquad a \cdot b \cdot c \neq 0 \qquad (3.12)$$

5. THE HOMOGENEOUS EQUATIONS, THE SECULAR EQUATION, AND THE SECULAR DETERMINANT

$$C_1 \overset{\bullet}{-} C_2$$

Let us consider one of the electrons in the π-molecular orbital of ethylene. The eigenfunction for this electron is a linear combination of p orbitals,

$$\psi = a_1 p_1 + a_2 p_2 \qquad (3.13)$$

where a_1 and a_2 remain to be determined.

The energy of an electron described by this eigenfunction is given by the Schrödinger equation as:

$$H\psi = E\psi$$

Multiplying both sides by ψ and integrating,

$$\int \psi H \psi \, dv = \int \psi E \psi \, dv$$

or

$$\int \psi H \psi \, dv = E \int \psi \psi \, dv$$

Transposing and solving for E,

$$E = \frac{\int \psi H \psi \, dv}{\int \psi \psi \, dv}$$

We do not assume here that ψ is normalized. Now, substitution of equation (3.13) for ψ results in

$$E = \frac{\int (a_1p_1 + a_2p_2)H(a_1p_1 + a_2p_2)\, dv}{\int (a_1p_1 + a_2p_2)(a_1p_1 + a_2p_2)\, dv}$$

Expansion of these integrals yields:

$$E = \frac{\int (a_1p_1Ha_1p_1 + a_1p_1Ha_2p_2 + a_2p_2Ha_1p_1 + a_2p_2Ha_2p_2)\, dv}{\int (a_1p_1a_1p_1 + a_1p_1a_2p_2 + a_2p_2a_1p_1 + a_2p_2a_2p_2)\, dv}$$

or

$$E = \frac{\int a_1p_1Ha_1p_1\, dv + \int a_1p_1Ha_2p_2\, dv + \int a_2p_2Ha_1p_1\, dv + \int a_2p_2Ha_2p_2\, dv}{\int a_1p_1a_1p_1\, dv + \int a_1p_1a_2p_2\, dv + \int a_2p_2a_1p_1\, dv + \int a_2p_2a_2p_2\, dv}$$

Since a_1 and a_2 are just numbers to be evaluated, they may be taken out from under the integral signs.

$$E = \frac{a_1{}^2 \int p_1Hp_1\, dv + a_1a_2 \int p_1Hp_2\, dv + a_1a_2 \int p_2Hp_1\, dv + a_2{}^2 \int p_2Hp_2\, dv}{a_1{}^2 \int p_1p_1\, dv + a_1a_2 \int p_1p_2\, dv + a_1a_2 \int p_2p_1\, dv + a_2{}^2 \int p_2p_2\, dv}$$

Now

$$\int p_1Hp_1\, dv = H_{11}$$

$$\int p_1Hp_2\, dv = H_{12}$$

$$\int p_2Hp_1\, dv = H_{21}$$

$$\int p_2Hp_2\, dv = H_{22}$$

and

$$\int p_1p_1\, dv = S_{11}$$

$$\int p_1 p_2 \, dv = S_{12}$$

$$\int p_2 p_1 \, dv = S_{21}$$

$$\int p_2 p_2 \, dv = S_{22}$$

Replacing each integral by its equivalent, we obtain:

$$E = \frac{a_1{}^2 H_{11} + a_1 a_2 H_{12} + a_1 a_2 H_{21} + a_2{}^2 H_{22}}{a_1{}^2 S_{11} + a_1 a_2 S_{12} + a_1 a_2 S_{21} + a_2{}^2 S_{22}}$$

Furthermore, we know that

$$H_{12} = H_{21} = \beta$$

Therefore, combination of the second and third terms in the numerator is possible. Similarly,

$$S_{12} = S_{21}$$

Therefore,

$$E = \frac{a_1{}^2 H_{11} + 2 a_1 a_2 H_{12} + a_2{}^2 H_{22}}{a_1{}^2 S_{11} + 2 a_1 a_2 S_{12} + a_2{}^2 S_{22}} \tag{3.14}$$

The only unknown quantities in equation (3.14) are a_1 and a_2. The calculated energy of the electron depends upon the values that we assign to a_1 and a_2, and we are interested in those values that minimize the energy of the electron. To minimize E one differentiates it first with respect to a_1 and sets the derivative equal to zero

$$\frac{\partial E}{\partial a_1} = 0$$

then with respect to a_2

$$\frac{\partial E}{\partial a_2} = 0$$

The expression on the right-hand side of equation (3.14) contains a_1 in both the numerator and the denominator. To differentiate this quotient with respect to a_1, one takes the denominator times the derivative of the numerator with respect to a_1 minus the numerator times the derivative of the denominator all over the square of the denominator.

$$\frac{\partial E}{\partial a_1} = \frac{(a_1{}^2 S_{11} + 2a_1 a_2 S_{12} + a_2{}^2 S_{22})(2a_1 H_{11} + 2a_2 H_{12})}{(a_1{}^2 S_{11} + 2a_1 a_2 S_{12} + a_2{}^2 S_{22})^2}$$

$$- \frac{(a_1{}^2 H_{11} + 2a_1 a_2 H_{12} + a_2{}^2 H_{22})(2a_1 S_{11} + 2a_2 S_{12})}{(a_1{}^2 S_{11} + 2a_1 a_2 S_{12} + a_2{}^2 S_{22})^2} = 0$$

Simplifying this expression, for the denominator times zero is still zero,

$$(a_1{}^2 S_{11} + 2a_1 a_2 S_{12} + a_2{}^2 S_{22})(2a_1 H_{11} + 2a_2 H_{12}) -$$

$$(a_1{}^2 H_{11} + 2a_1 a_2 H_{12} + a_2{}^2 H_{22})(2a_1 S_{11} + 2a_2 S_{12}) = 0$$

or

$$(a_1{}^2 S_{11} + 2a_1 a_2 S_{12} + a_2{}^2 S_{22})(2a_1 H_{11} + 2a_2 H_{12}) =$$

$$(a_1{}^2 H_{11} + 2a_1 a_2 H_{12} + a_2{}^2 H_{22})(2a_1 S_{11} + 2a_2 S_{12})$$

Transposing and dividing each side by 2,

$$a_1 H_{11} + a_2 H_{12} = \left(\frac{a_1{}^2 H_{11} + 2a_1 a_2 H_{12} + a_2{}^2 H_{22}}{a_1{}^2 S_{11} + 2a_1 a_2 S_{12} + a_2{}^2 S_{22}} \right) (a_1 S_{11} + a_2 S_{12}) \quad (3.15)$$

The first term on the right side of (3.15) is just E (see equation 3.14). Substitution gives:

$$a_1 H_{11} + a_2 H_{12} = E(a_1 S_{11} + a_2 S_{12})$$

or

$$a_1 H_{11} + a_2 H_{12} = a_1 S_{11} E + a_2 S_{12} E$$

Finally we obtain:

$$a_1 (H_{11} - S_{11} E) + a_2 (H_{12} - S_{12} E) = 0$$

Minimizing E with respect to a_2 gives a similar equation.

$$a_1 (H_{21} - S_{21} E) + a_2 (H_{22} - S_{22} E) = 0$$

We have obtained two homogeneous linear equations that must be satisfied.

$$a_1(H_{11} - S_{11}E) + a_2(H_{12} - S_{12}E) = 0$$

$$a_1(H_{21} - S_{21}E) + a_2(H_{22} - S_{22}E) = 0 \qquad (3.16)$$

These two equations must be simultaneously satisfied in order to find the allowed values of E. From them, one also obtains the desired values of a_1 and a_2. Before continuing, let us generalize this result to the case of n carbon atoms each having a p orbital. Here ψ becomes:

$$\psi = a_1 p_1 + a_2 p_2 + a_3 p_3 + \cdots + a_n p_n$$

and the generalized homogeneous linear equations take the form,

$$a_1(H_{11} - S_{11}E) + a_2(H_{12} - S_{12}E) + \cdots + a_n(H_{1n} - S_{1n}E) = 0$$
$$a_1(H_{21} - S_{21}E) + a_2(H_{22} - S_{22}E) + \cdots + a_n(H_{2n} - S_{2n}E) = 0$$
$$a_1(H_{31} - S_{31}E) + a_2(H_{32} - S_{32}E) + \cdots + a_n(H_{3n} - S_{3n}E) = 0$$

$$\cdots$$

$$\cdots$$

$$\cdots$$

$$a_1(H_{n1} - S_{n1}E) + a_2(H_{n2} - S_{n2}E) + \cdots + a_n(H_{nn} - S_{nn}E) = 0 \qquad (3.17)$$

Expression (3.16) may be rewritten in determinant form.

$$\begin{vmatrix} a_1(H_{11} - S_{11}E) & a_2(H_{12} - S_{12}E) \\ a_1(H_{21} - S_{21}E) & a_2(H_{22} - S_{22}E) \end{vmatrix} = 0$$

Factoring out a_1 and a_2,

$$a_1 \cdot a_2 \begin{vmatrix} H_{11} - S_{11}E & H_{12} - S_{12}E \\ H_{21} - S_{21}E & H_{22} - S_{22}E \end{vmatrix} = 0 \qquad (3.18)$$

Since a_1 and a_2 are not zero, this condition can be satisfied only if the determinant equals zero. Therefore,

$$\begin{vmatrix} H_{11} - S_{11}E & H_{12} - S_{12}E \\ H_{21} - S_{21}E & H_{22} - S_{22}E \end{vmatrix} = 0 \qquad (3.19)$$

This equation is the *secular* equation for ethylene and the determinant is called the secular determinant for ethylene. Solving expression (3.19) for E gives the energy of an electron in the various π-molecular orbitals of ethylene. The values of a_1 and a_2 are found from the homogeneous equations (3.16), after E has been obtained. A similar treatment of (3.17) gives the generalized secular equation.

$$
\begin{vmatrix}
H_{11} - S_{11}E & H_{12} - S_{12}E & H_{13} - S_{13}E & \cdots & H_{1n} - S_{1n}E \\
H_{21} - S_{21}E & H_{22} - S_{22}E & H_{23} - S_{23}E & \cdots & H_{2n} - S_{2n}E \\
H_{31} - S_{31}E & H_{32} - S_{32}E & H_{33} - S_{33}E & \cdots & H_{3n} - S_{3n}E \\
\cdot & \cdot & \cdot & \cdots & \cdot \\
\cdot & \cdot & \cdot & \cdots & \cdot \\
\cdot & \cdot & \cdot & \cdots & \cdot \\
H_{n1} - S_{n1}E & H_{n2} - S_{n2}E & H_{n3} - S_{n3}E & \cdots & H_{nn} - S_{nn}E
\end{vmatrix} = 0 \qquad (3.20)
$$

Solving this secular equation for E gives the allowed energy levels for an electron in molecular orbitals spanning n carbon atoms. Each value of E corresponds to the energy of a molecular orbital.

In chapter four we shall evaluate the coefficients $a_1, a_2, a_3, \cdots, a_n$. For the remainder of this chapter we calculate the π-electronic energies of some simple alkenes and see how the ideas that we have developed so far are used. Remember that the following values have been assigned to the terms that appear in the secular determinant,

$$H_{AA} = \alpha$$

$$H_{AB} = \begin{cases} \beta & \text{if } A \text{ and } B \text{ are adjacent carbon atoms} \\ 0 & \text{if } A \text{ and } B \text{ are nonadjacent atoms} \end{cases}$$

$$S_{AA} = 1$$

$$S_{AB} = 0 \qquad (3.21)$$

6. CALCULATION OF THE ENERGIES OF Π-MOLECULAR ORBITALS

The procedure that is followed was outlined in section 3.1. The energy of an electron in the various molecular orbitals is calculated; then each orbital accommodates two electrons of opposite spin.

6.1. ETHYLENE

The eigenfunction for the electron is:

$$\psi = a_1 p_1 + a_2 p_2$$

and the secular equation was shown to be

$$\begin{vmatrix} H_{11} - S_{11}E & H_{12} - S_{12}E \\ H_{21} - S_{21}E & H_{22} - S_{22}E \end{vmatrix} = 0$$

Solving this equation for E gives the allowed energy levels for the electron. Substituting,

$$H_{11} = H_{22} = \alpha$$

$$H_{12} = H_{21} = \beta$$

$$S_{11} = S_{22} = 1$$

$$S_{12} = S_{21} = 0$$

Our determinant now becomes

$$\begin{vmatrix} \alpha - E & \beta \\ \beta & \alpha - E \end{vmatrix} = 0$$

Dividing each term by β, we obtain

$$\begin{vmatrix} \dfrac{\alpha - E}{\beta} & 1 \\ 1 & \dfrac{\alpha - E}{\beta} \end{vmatrix} = 0$$

Let us make the substitution

$$x = \frac{\alpha - E}{\beta} \tag{3.22}$$

and our determinant when written in terms of x is:

$$\begin{vmatrix} x & 1 \\ 1 & x \end{vmatrix} = 0$$

Expansion of this determinant gives the polynomial equation

$$x^2 - 1 = 0$$

or

$$x = -1, \quad x = 1$$

Replacing x by its equivalent (3.22) and solving for E,

$$x = -1$$

$$\frac{\alpha - E}{\beta} = -1$$

$$E_1 = \alpha + \beta$$

$$x = 1$$

$$\frac{\alpha - E}{\beta} = 1$$

$$E_2 = \alpha - \beta$$

We find two permissible energy levels for our electron. In the ground state the electron is in the molecular orbital ψ_1, corresponding to the energy, $\alpha + \beta$. Since ethylene has two electrons in the π bond, both are placed in this bonding orbital (see Figure 3–7). The total energy of the system of two electrons is then,

$$E = 2E_1$$

$$E = 2\alpha + 2\beta$$

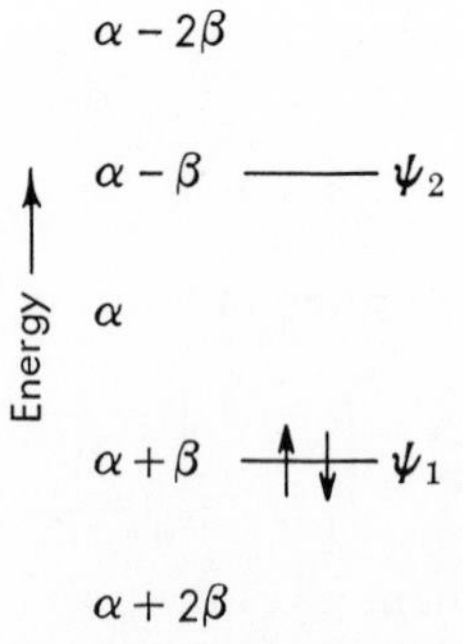

$$\alpha - 2\beta$$

$$\alpha - \beta \quad \text{——} \quad \psi_2$$

$$\alpha$$

$$\alpha + \beta \quad \text{—↑↓—} \quad \psi_1$$

$$\alpha + 2\beta$$

FIGURE 3–7 THE ENERGY OF THE
TWO π-ELECTRONS IN ETHYLENE

The energy of an electron in a p atomic orbital is α, and the two electrons would have energy 2α. The energy of π-bond formation is

$$2\alpha + 2\beta - 2\alpha = 2\beta$$

6.2. The Allyl System

The eigenfunction for the electron is:

$$\psi = a_1 p_1 + a_2 p_2 + a_3 p_3$$

and the secular determinant is one of third order.

$$\begin{vmatrix} H_{11} - S_{11}E & H_{12} - S_{12}E & H_{13} - S_{13}E \\ H_{21} - S_{21}E & H_{22} - S_{22}E & H_{23} - S_{23}E \\ H_{31} - S_{31}E & H_{32} - S_{32}E & H_{33} - S_{33}E \end{vmatrix} = 0$$

Now,

$$H_{11} = H_{22} = H_{33} = \alpha$$

$$H_{12} = H_{21} = H_{23} = H_{32} = \beta$$

$$H_{13} = H_{31} = 0$$

$$S_{11} = S_{22} = S_{33} = 1$$

$$S_{12} = S_{21} = S_{13} = S_{31} = S_{23} = S_{32} = 0$$

Substitution yields:

$$\begin{vmatrix} \alpha - E & \beta & 0 \\ \beta & \alpha - E & \beta \\ 0 & \beta & \alpha - E \end{vmatrix} = 0$$

Dividing by β and letting $x = (\alpha - E)/\beta$,

$$\begin{vmatrix} x & 1 & 0 \\ 1 & x & 1 \\ 0 & 1 & x \end{vmatrix} = 0$$

Upon expansion, the polynomial equation is:

$$x^3 - 2x = 0$$

which has the roots

$$x = -\sqrt{2}, \quad x = 0, \quad x = \sqrt{2}$$

Replacing x by $(\alpha - E)/\beta$ and solving for E,

$$x = -\sqrt{2}$$

$$E_1 = \alpha + \sqrt{2}\beta$$

and

$$x = 0$$

$$E_2 = \alpha$$

$$x = \sqrt{2}$$

$$E_3 = \alpha - \sqrt{2}\beta$$

The two π-electrons present in the allyl carbonium ion are both placed in ψ_1 with total energy

$$E_{C_3H_5(+)} = 2(\alpha + \sqrt{2}\beta)$$

$$= 2\alpha + 2\sqrt{2}\beta$$

The allyl radical has three electrons, and the third one must go into ψ_2 (see Figure 3–8). Consequently, the total π-electronic energy of the allyl radical is:

$$E_{C_3H_5(\cdot)} = 2(\alpha + \sqrt{2}\beta) + \alpha$$

$$= 3\alpha + 2\sqrt{2}\beta$$

In the allyl carbanion still another electron must be accommodated. This is also put into ψ_2. The anion has two electrons in ψ_1 and two in ψ_2 with total energy

$$E_{C_3H_5(-)} = 2(\alpha + \sqrt{2}\beta) + 2\alpha$$

$$= 4\alpha + 2\sqrt{2}\beta$$

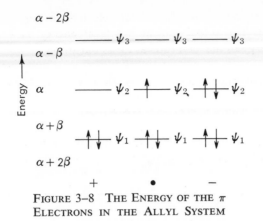

FIGURE 3–8 THE ENERGY OF THE π
ELECTRONS IN THE ALLYL SYSTEM

The resonance energy of the allyl carbonium ion is the energy difference between the structure on the left of Figure 3–9 (here the electrons are localized in the double bond, and the compound has no resonance stabilization), and the energy of the actual molecule. This structure with delocalized electrons is depicted on the right.

$$C=C-\overset{+}{C} \qquad \overset{\delta^+}{C}\!=\!=\!\overset{\delta^+}{C}\!=\!=\!C$$

FIGURE 3–9   THE ALLYL CARBONIUM ION
WITH LOCALIZED AND DELOCALIZED ELECTRONS

The difference in the energy of these two structures is just the difference in the energy of the two electrons comprising the π bond. Nothing else has changed. The localized structure has the two electrons in an ethylenic unit with energy $2\alpha + 2\beta$ (the same energy as that of the two electrons in ethylene) while the actual allyl carbonium ion has the two electrons in ψ_1 with energy $2\alpha + 2\sqrt{2}\,\beta$. The resonance energy is:

$$\text{resonance energy} = 2\alpha + 2\beta - (2\alpha + 2\sqrt{2}\beta)$$

$$\text{resonance energy} = -0.828\beta$$

The resonance energy of the allyl radical is calculated in a similar fashion (see Figure 3–10). The localized structure has two electrons in an ethylenic

$$C=C-\overset{\bullet}{C} \qquad \overset{\delta^\bullet}{C}\!=\!=\!\overset{\delta^\bullet}{C}\!=\!=\!C$$

FIGURE 3–10   THE ALLYL RADICAL WITH
LOCALIZED AND DELOCALIZED ELECTRONS

linkage with energy $2\alpha + 2\beta$ and one electron in an isolated p orbital with energy α. The actual radical has total energy $3\alpha + 2\sqrt{2}\beta$, and the resonance energy of the allyl radical turns out to be

$$\text{resonance energy} = 2\alpha + 2\beta + \alpha - (3\alpha + 2\sqrt{2}\beta)$$

$$\text{resonance energy} = -0.828\beta$$

Figure 3–11 illustrates the situation for the anion. There are now two electrons in the p atomic orbital and

$$\text{resonance energy} = 2\alpha + 2\beta + 2\alpha - (4\alpha + 2\sqrt{2}\beta)$$

$$\text{resonance energy} = -0.828\beta$$

$$\text{C}=\text{C}-\bar{\text{C}} \qquad \overset{\delta^-}{\text{C}}{\cdots}\text{C}{\cdots}\overset{\delta^-}{\text{C}}$$

FIGURE 3–11 THE ALLYL CARBANION
WITH LOCALIZED AND DELOCALIZED ELECTRONS

It is not surprising that the resonance energy of all three systems is identical. In the localized structures, in going from the carbonium ion to the radical to the carbanion, we are placing electrons in an isolated p orbital of energy α. In the actual molecule we put the electrons into a nonbonding molecular orbital having energy α. The energy difference, the resonance energy, remains constant.

6.3. THE CYCLOPROPENYL SYSTEM

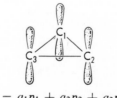

$$\psi = a_1p_1 + a_2p_2 + a_3p_3$$

The secular equation is:

$$\begin{vmatrix} H_{11} - S_{11}E & H_{12} - S_{12}E & H_{13} - S_{13}E \\ H_{21} - S_{21}E & H_{22} - S_{22}E & H_{23} - S_{23}E \\ H_{31} - S_{31}E & H_{32} - S_{32}E & H_{33} - S_{33}E \end{vmatrix} = 0$$

and

$$H_{11} = H_{22} = H_{33} = \alpha$$

$$H_{12} = H_{21} = H_{13} = H_{31} = H_{23} = H_{32} = \beta$$

$$S_{11} = S_{22} = S_{33} = 1$$

$$S_{12} = S_{21} = S_{13} = S_{31} = S_{23} = S_{32} = 0$$

Notice that H_{13} and H_{31} are now equal to β since carbon atoms 1 and 3 are bonded (adjacent). In terms of the parameters the determinant becomes:

$$\begin{vmatrix} \alpha - E & \beta & \beta \\ \beta & \alpha - E & \beta \\ \beta & \beta & \alpha - E \end{vmatrix} = 0$$

Carrying out the usual procedure we obtain:

$$\begin{vmatrix} x & 1 & 1 \\ 1 & x & 1 \\ 1 & 1 & x \end{vmatrix} = 0$$

where

$$x = \frac{\alpha - E}{\beta}$$

The resulting equation is:

$$x^3 - 3x + 2 = 0$$

and the roots to this equation are:

$$x = -2, \quad x = 1, \quad x = 1$$

$$x = -2$$
$$E_1 = \alpha + 2\beta$$

$$x = 1$$
$$E_2 = \alpha - \beta$$

$$x = 1$$
$$E_3 = \alpha - \beta$$

Here, we encounter degenerate orbitals for the first time. The energy of ψ_2 and ψ_3 is the same, for both have associated with them an energy $\alpha - \beta$. The cyclopropenyl carbonium ion has both π electrons in ψ_1

$$E_{C_3H_3(+)} = 2(\alpha + 2\beta)$$

$$= 2\alpha + 4\beta$$

while the cyclopropenyl carbanion has two electrons in ψ_1, one electron in ψ_2, and one in ψ_3, as shown in Figure 3–12.

$$E_{C_3H_3(-)} = (2\alpha + 4\beta) + (\alpha - \beta) + (\alpha - \beta)$$

$$= 4\alpha + 2\beta$$

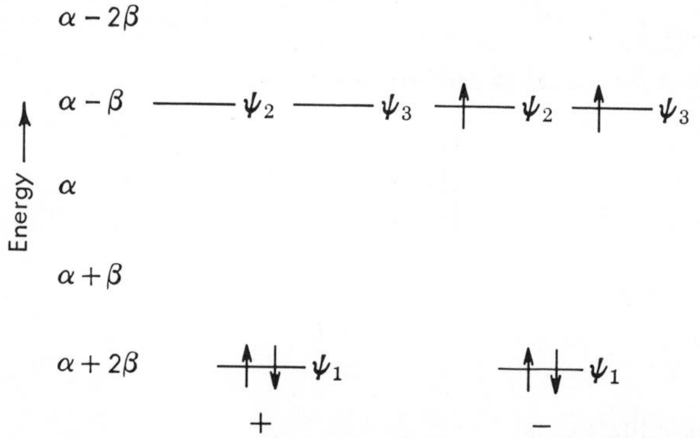

FIGURE 3–12   THE ENERGY OF THE π ELECTRONS IN THE CYCLOPROPENYL CARBONIUM ION AND CARBANION

The resonance energy of the carbonium ion is found to be:

$$\text{resonance energy} = 2\alpha + 2\beta - (2\alpha + 4\beta)$$

$$\text{resonance energy} = -2\beta$$

while that of the carbanion is:

$$\text{resonance energy} = 4\alpha + 2\beta - (4\alpha + 2\beta)$$

$$\text{resonance energy} = 0$$

The carbonium ion is predicted to be very stable. Much more stable in fact than the allyl carbonium ion, which we know to be stable. The cyclopropenyl carbanion, on the other hand, has no resonance stabilization and is predicted by the Hückel theory to exist as a diradical. These results exemplify Hückel's $4n + 2$ rule where n equals zero.

The unstrained bond angles for sp^2 hybridized carbon atoms are 120°. Consequently, the considerable ring strain that must be present in the cyclopropenyl carbonium ion should make this intermediate extremely unstable, yet the fact that hydride ions are readily abstracted from cyclopropene[6] suggests stability for this cation.

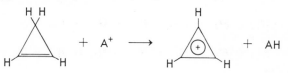

In addition, molecular-orbital calculations[7] predict exceptional stability for the triphenyl cation (III), and this is substantiated. The di-n-propylcyclopropenyl (I)[8], the diphenylcyclopropenyl (II),[9] and the triphenylcyclopropenyl (III)[10] carbonium ions are all stable, some derivatives existing as salts even in the solid state.

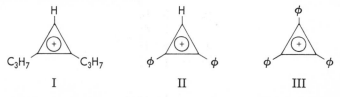

The experimental data uniformly illustrate exceptional stabilization of the carbonium ions in good accord with the Hückel theory.

Concerning the cyclopropenyl carbanion, not much information is available. What research has been done regarding its stability supports the idea that this anion is unstable although its diradical character is questionable.

6.4. BUTADIENE

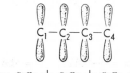

$$\psi = a_1 p_1 + a_2 p_2 + a_3 p_3 + a_4 p_4$$

[6] K. B. Wiberg, Abstracts of Papers, ACS meeting, April 7–12, 1957, Miami, Fla., p. 39–O.
[7] A. Streitwieser, Jr., *J. Am. Chem. Soc.*, **82,** 4123 (1960).
[8] R. Breslow and H. Höver, *J. Am. Chem. Soc.*, **82,** 2644 (1960).
[9] D. G. Farnum and M. Burr, *J. Am. Chem. Soc.*, **82,** 2651 (1960).
[10] R. Breslow and C. Yuan, *J. Am. Chem. Soc.*, **80,** 5991 (1958).

$$\begin{vmatrix} H_{11} - S_{11}E & H_{12} - S_{12}E & H_{13} - S_{13}E & H_{14} - S_{14}E \\ H_{21} - S_{21}E & H_{22} - S_{22}E & H_{23} - S_{23}E & H_{24} - S_{24}E \\ H_{31} - S_{31}E & H_{32} - S_{32}E & H_{33} - S_{33}E & H_{34} - S_{34}E \\ H_{41} - S_{41}E & H_{42} - S_{42}E & H_{43} - S_{43}E & H_{44} - S_{44}E \end{vmatrix} = 0$$

and

$$H_{11} = H_{22} = H_{33} = H_{44} = \alpha$$

$$H_{12} = H_{21} = H_{23} = H_{32} = H_{34} = H_{43} = \beta$$

$$H_{13} = H_{31} = H_{14} = H_{41} = H_{24} = H_{42} = 0$$

$$S_{11} = S_{22} = S_{33} = S_{44} = 1$$

$$\text{all } S_{AB} \quad A \neq B = 0$$

The usual procedure gives:

$$\begin{vmatrix} x & 1 & 0 & 0 \\ 1 & x & 1 & 0 \\ 0 & 1 & x & 1 \\ 0 & 0 & 1 & x \end{vmatrix} = 0$$

or

$$x \begin{vmatrix} x & 1 & 0 \\ 1 & x & 1 \\ 0 & 1 & x \end{vmatrix} - 1 \begin{vmatrix} 1 & 1 & 0 \\ 0 & x & 1 \\ 0 & 1 & x \end{vmatrix} = 0$$

The resulting polynomial equation is

$$x^4 - 3x^2 + 1 = 0$$

which has the roots

$$x = -1.62, \quad x = -0.618, \quad x = 0.618, \quad x = 1.62$$

$$x = -1.62$$
$$E_1 = \alpha + 1.62\beta$$

$$x = -0.618$$
$$E_2 = \alpha + 0.618\beta$$

$$x = 0.618$$

$$E_3 = \alpha - 0.618\beta$$

$$x = 1.62$$

$$E_4 = \alpha - 1.62\beta$$

The four π-electrons fill the two orbitals of lowest energy (see Figure 3–13).

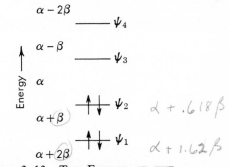

FIGURE 3–13   THE ENERGY OF THE FOUR π-ELECTRONS IN BUTADIENE

The total π-electronic energy of butadiene is:

$$E = 2(\alpha + 1.62\beta) + 2(\alpha + 0.618\beta)$$

$$E = 4\alpha + 4.48\beta$$

and the resonance energy of butadiene is the difference between the energy of the structure having two localized double bonds, each ethylenic linkage having energy $2\alpha + 2\beta$, and the actual energy.

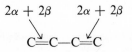

$$2\alpha + 2\beta \qquad 2\alpha + 2\beta$$

$$C{=}C{-}C{=}C$$

resonance energy $= 2(2\alpha + 2\beta) - (4\alpha + 4.48\beta)$

resonance energy $= -0.48\beta$

6.5. CYCLOBUTADIENE[11]

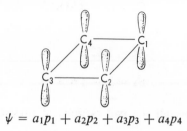

$$\psi = a_1 p_1 + a_2 p_2 + a_3 p_3 + a_4 p_4$$

Perkin in 1894, first attempted the synthesis of a cyclobutadiene deriva-tive, the dicarboxylic acid.[12] This, like so many later tries by other

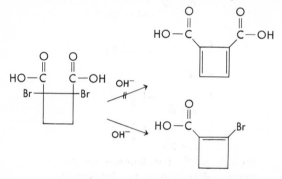

investigators, was unsuccessful. Eleven years later, Willstätter and Schmaedel fared no better though they were after the parent compound.[13]

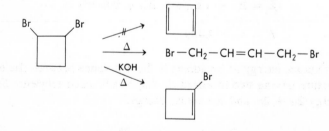

---

[11] For an excellent discussion concerning cyclobutadiene and its derivatives, see Chapter II by W. Baker and J. F. W. McOmie in *Non-Benzenoid Aromatic Compounds*, D. Ginsberg (ed.), Interscience, New York, 1959.

[12] W. H. Perkin, Jr., *J. Chem. Soc.*, **65**, 967 (1894).

[13] R. Willstätter and W. v. Schmaedel, *Ber.*, **38**, 1992 (1905).

The literature contains many other attempts by a large number of investigators, and some of these are presented. The pyrolysis of quarternary ammonium hydroxides leads to several products.[14,15]

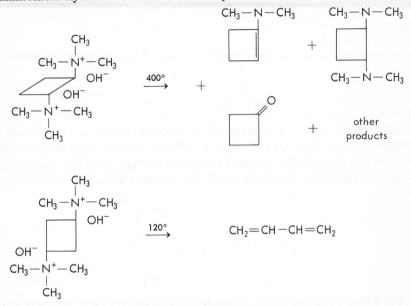

In 1957, Criegee and Louis reported that the action of lithium amalgam on the dichloride (IV) resulted in the formation of a dimer of the desired cyclobutadiene.[16]

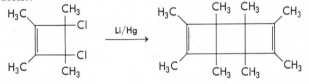

IV

Still another approach involved a Diels-Alder reaction of the di-exomethylenecyclobutene (V)[17], but this compound gave no adduct at all with maleic anhydride while reaction with tetracyanoethylene resulted in 1,2-addition. The results are illustrated schematically.

[14] E. R. Buchman, M. J. Schlatter, and A. O. Reims, *J. Am. Chem. Soc.*, **64**, 2701 (1942).

[15] M. Avram, C. D. Nenitzescu, and E. Marica, *Ber.*, **90**, 1857 (1957).

[16] R. Criegee and G. Louis, *Ber.*, **90**, 417 (1957).

[17] A. T. Blomquist and Y. C. Meinwald, *J. Am. Chem. Soc.*, **81**, 667 (1959).

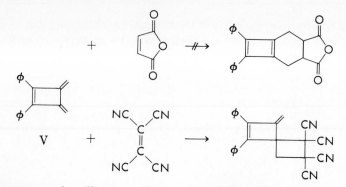

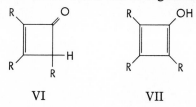

Attempts at the direct synthesis of cyclobutadiene and substituted cyclobutadienes have failed. Using a different line of reasoning several authors investigated the chemistry of cyclobutenones (VI). The enols (VII) of these compounds are dienes which can be regarded as cyclobutadienes.

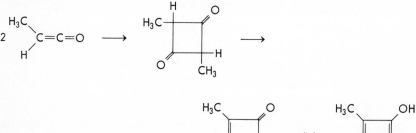

VI   VII

The structure of one of the products of the dimerization of methylketene has been elucidated by Woodward and Small.[18] This substance, mono-enolic, shows no tendency to form the di-enol.

Roberts, Kline, and Simmons prepared the cyclobutenone (VIII).[19] This product gave no color with ferric chloride, and its infrared absorption spectrum contained no —OH band.

---

[18] R. B. Woodward and G. Small, *J. Am. Chem. Soc.*, **72**, 1297 (1950).
[19] J. D. Roberts, G. B. Kline, and H. E. Simmons, *J. Am. Chem. Soc.*, **75**, 4765 (1953).

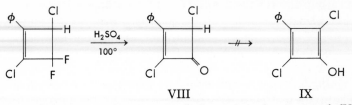

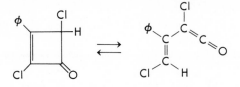

VIII   IX

Jenny and Roberts partially resolved the carbonyl compound (VIII)[20] and measured the loss of optical activity, yet this process did not involve the cyclobutadiene (IX). Instead a ketene was shown to be the intermediate.

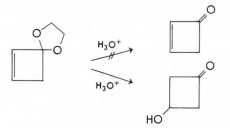

In 1958, Vogel and Hasse synthesized a cyclobutenone ketal,[21] but hydrolysis of this material yields no cyclobutenone.

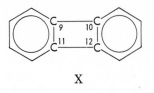

One compound often regarded as a cyclobutadiene derivative is biphenylene (X). This material, prepared using a variety of techniques, appears quite stable, in sharp contrast to the substances discussed previously.

X

A structural elucidation of X by the method of electron diffraction[22] discloses the fact that the bonds joining the benzene rings (the bonds

[20] E. F. Jenny and J. D. Roberts, *J. Am. Chem. Soc.*, **78,** 2005 (1956).
[21] E. Vogel and K. Hasse, *Ann.*, **615,** 22 (1958).
[22] J. Waser and V. Schomaker, *J. Am. Chem. Soc.*, **65,** 1451 (1943)

joining carbon atoms 9 to 10, and 11 to 12) have approximately the normal single bond lengths, and this idea is confirmed by x-ray crystallography.[23] Thus, little, if any, resonance stabilization of the four-membered ring is present, and the stability of X stems from the stability of the six-membered rings.

The synthesis of cyclobutadiene and its derivatives by conventional means fails. The strain that must be present in a four-membered ring of this type is considerable. Weltner reports a value of 47–62 kcal/mole where the value depends upon the choice of bond strengths.[24] Nevertheless, the cyclopropenyl system contains more strain, and compounds in this series have been prepared. One must conclude that cyclobutadiene is unstable and that this instability is not due to ring strain but due to lack of resonance stabilization.

While cyclobutadiene remains inaccessible, theoretical calculations predict the stability of its metal complexes,[25] and attempts at the preparation of these materials have been extremely successful. Freedman has reported the preparation of the nickel bromide complex of tetraphenylcyclobutadiene,[26] Criegee and Schröder the nickel chloride complex of tetramethylcyclobutadiene,[27] and Avram, Marica, and Nenitzescu the silver nitrate complex of cyclobutadiene, itself.[28]

A valence-bond calculation predicts stability for cyclobutadiene, assigning to it a structure having paired electrons and a resonance energy of 30 kcal/mole.[29] In contrast, a Hückel molecular-orbital calculation claims instability for the compound but assigns a diradical ground state to the molecule. We carry out the Hückel calculation.

The secular equation for cyclobutadiene is:

$$\begin{vmatrix} H_{11} - S_{11}E & H_{12} - S_{12}E & H_{13} - S_{13}E & H_{14} - S_{14}E \\ H_{21} - S_{21}E & H_{22} - S_{22}E & H_{23} - S_{23}E & H_{24} - S_{24}E \\ H_{31} - S_{31}E & H_{32} - S_{32}E & H_{33} - S_{33}E & H_{34} - S_{34}E \\ H_{41} - S_{41}E & H_{42} - S_{42}E & H_{43} - S_{43}E & H_{44} - S_{44}E \end{vmatrix} = 0$$

[23] J. Waser and C. S. Lu, *J. Am. Chem. Soc.*, **66**, 2035 (1944).
[24] W. Weltner, Jr., *J. Am. Chem. Soc.*, **75**, 4224 (1953).
[25] H. C. Longuet-Higgins and L. E. Orgel, *J. Chem. Soc.*, 1 (1956).
[26] H. H. Freedman, *J. Am. Chem. Soc.*, **83**, 2194, 2195 (1961).
[27] R. Criegee and G. Schröder, *Ann.*, **623**, 1 (1959).
[28] M. Avram, E. Marica, and C. D. Nenitzescu, *Ber.*, **92**, 1088 (1959).
[29] See the chapter by D. P. Craig in *Non-Benzenoid Aromatic Compounds*, D. Gingsberg (ed.), Interscience, New York, 1959. See also G. W. Wheland, *Resonance in Organic Chemistry*, Wiley, New York, 1955, p. 142.

Remember that $H_{14} = H_{41} = \beta$ in this case. In terms of x the determinant becomes:

$$\begin{vmatrix} x & 1 & 0 & 1 \\ 1 & x & 1 & 0 \\ 0 & 1 & x & 1 \\ 1 & 0 & 1 & x \end{vmatrix} = 0$$

where

$$x = \frac{\alpha - E}{\beta}$$

Expanding,

$$x\begin{vmatrix} x & 1 & 0 \\ 1 & x & 1 \\ 0 & 1 & x \end{vmatrix} - 1\begin{vmatrix} 1 & 1 & 0 \\ 0 & x & 1 \\ 1 & 1 & x \end{vmatrix} - 1\begin{vmatrix} 1 & x & 1 \\ 0 & 1 & x \\ 1 & 0 & 1 \end{vmatrix} = 0$$

$$x^4 - 4x^2 = 0$$

The roots of this equation are:

$$x = -2, \quad x = 0, \quad x = 0, \quad x = 2$$

$$x = -2$$
$$E_1 = \alpha + 2\beta \qquad \psi_1$$

$$x = 0$$
$$E_2 = \alpha \qquad \psi_2$$

$$x = 0$$
$$E_3 = \alpha \qquad \psi_3$$

$$x = 2$$
$$E_4 = \alpha - 2\beta \qquad \psi_4$$

Again we find degeneracy between ψ_2 and ψ_3. Two π-electrons are accommodated in ψ_1, one in ψ_2, and one in ψ_3 (see Figure 3–14). The total energy of the four electrons is

$$E = 2(\alpha + 2\beta) + \alpha + \alpha$$

$$E = 4\alpha + 4\beta$$

and the resonance energy of cyclobutadiene is predicted to be:

$$\text{resonance energy} = 2(2\alpha + 2\beta) - (4\alpha + 4\beta)$$

$$\text{resonance energy} = 0$$

where the first term is the π-electronic energy of the localized structure.

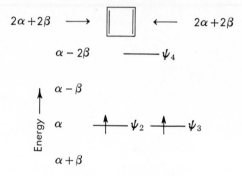

FIGURE 3–14   THE ENERGY OF THE
FOUR π-ELECTRONS IN CYCLOBUTADIENE

6.6. TRIMETHYLENEMETHANE

$$\psi = a_1 p_1 + a_2 p_2 + a_3 p_3 + a_4 p_4$$

$$\begin{vmatrix} H_{11} - S_{11}E & H_{12} - S_{12}E & H_{13} - S_{13}E & H_{14} - S_{14}E \\ H_{21} - S_{21}E & H_{22} - S_{22}E & H_{23} - S_{23}E & H_{24} - S_{24}E \\ H_{31} - S_{31}E & H_{32} - S_{32}E & H_{33} - S_{33}E & H_{34} - S_{34}E \\ H_{41} - S_{41}E & H_{42} - S_{42}E & H_{43} - S_{43}E & H_{44} - S_{44}E \end{vmatrix} = 0$$

$$H_{14} = H_{41} = H_{24} = H_{42} = H_{34} = H_{43} = \beta$$

all other $H_{AB}, A \neq B, = 0$

Making the appropriate substitutions and rewriting the determinant, we have

$$\begin{vmatrix} x & 0 & 0 & 1 \\ 0 & x & 0 & 1 \\ 0 & 0 & x & 1 \\ 1 & 1 & 1 & x \end{vmatrix} = 0$$

$$x \begin{vmatrix} x & 0 & 1 \\ 0 & x & 1 \\ 1 & 1 & x \end{vmatrix} - 1 \begin{vmatrix} 0 & x & 0 \\ 0 & 0 & x \\ 1 & 1 & 1 \end{vmatrix} = 0$$

or

$$x^4 - 3x^2 = 0$$

then

$$x = -\sqrt{3}, \qquad x = 0, \qquad x = 0, \qquad x = \sqrt{3}$$

$$x = -\sqrt{3}$$
$$E_1 = \alpha + \sqrt{3}\beta$$

$$x = 0$$
$$E_2 = \alpha$$

$$x = 0$$
$$E_3 = \alpha$$

$$x = \sqrt{3}$$
$$E_4 = \alpha - \sqrt{3}\beta$$

There are four electrons in this system, and their total energy is

$$E = 4\alpha + 2\sqrt{3}\beta$$

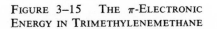

FIGURE 3–15   THE π-ELECTRONIC ENERGY IN TRIMETHYLENEMETHANE

6.7. The Cyclopentadienyl System

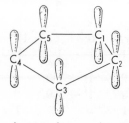

$$\psi = a_1p_1 + a_2p_2 + a_3p_3 + a_4p_4 + a_5p_5$$

and

$$\begin{vmatrix} H_{11} - S_{11}E & H_{12} - S_{12}E & H_{13} - S_{13}E & H_{14} - S_{14}E & H_{15} - S_{15}E \\ H_{21} - S_{21}E & H_{22} - S_{22}E & H_{23} - S_{23}E & H_{24} - S_{24}E & H_{25} - S_{25}E \\ H_{31} - S_{31}E & H_{32} - S_{32}E & H_{33} - S_{33}E & H_{34} - S_{34}E & H_{35} - S_{35}E \\ H_{41} - S_{41}E & H_{42} - S_{42}E & H_{43} - S_{43}E & H_{44} - S_{44}E & H_{45} - S_{45}E \\ H_{51} - S_{51}E & H_{52} - S_{52}E & H_{53} - S_{53}E & H_{54} - S_{54}E & H_{55} - S_{55}E \end{vmatrix} = 0$$

$$\begin{vmatrix} x & 1 & 0 & 0 & 1 \\ 1 & x & 1 & 0 & 0 \\ 0 & 1 & x & 1 & 0 \\ 0 & 0 & 1 & x & 1 \\ 1 & 0 & 0 & 1 & x \end{vmatrix} = 0$$

Solving—

$$x\begin{vmatrix} x & 1 & 0 & 0 \\ 1 & x & 1 & 0 \\ 0 & 1 & x & 1 \\ 0 & 0 & 1 & x \end{vmatrix} - 1\begin{vmatrix} 1 & 1 & 0 & 0 \\ 0 & x & 1 & 0 \\ 0 & 1 & x & 1 \\ 1 & 0 & 1 & x \end{vmatrix} + 1\begin{vmatrix} 1 & x & 1 & 0 \\ 0 & 1 & x & 1 \\ 0 & 0 & 1 & x \\ 1 & 0 & 0 & 1 \end{vmatrix} = 0$$

Now,

$$x^2\begin{vmatrix} x & 1 & 0 \\ 1 & x & 1 \\ 0 & 1 & x \end{vmatrix} - x\begin{vmatrix} 1 & 1 & 0 \\ 0 & x & 1 \\ 0 & 1 & x \end{vmatrix} - 1\begin{vmatrix} x & 1 & 0 \\ 1 & x & 1 \\ 0 & 1 & x \end{vmatrix} + 1\begin{vmatrix} 0 & 1 & 0 \\ 0 & x & 1 \\ 1 & 1 & x \end{vmatrix}$$

$$+ 1\begin{vmatrix} 1 & x & 1 \\ 0 & 1 & x \\ 0 & 0 & 1 \end{vmatrix} - x\begin{vmatrix} 0 & x & 1 \\ 0 & 1 & x \\ 1 & 0 & 1 \end{vmatrix} + 1\begin{vmatrix} 0 & 1 & 1 \\ 0 & 0 & x \\ 1 & 0 & 1 \end{vmatrix} = 0$$

The resulting polynomial equation is

$$x^5 - 5x^3 + 5x + 2 = 0$$

and the roots are:

$$x = -2.00, \qquad x = -0.618, \qquad x = -0.618,$$

$$x = 1.62, \qquad x = 1.62.$$

$$x = -2.00$$
$$E_1 = \alpha + 2.00\beta$$

$$x = -0.618$$
$$E_2 = \alpha + 0.618\beta$$

$$x = -0.618$$
$$E_3 = \alpha + 0.618\beta$$

$$x = 1.62$$
$$E_4 = \alpha - 1.62\beta$$

$$x = 1.62$$
$$E_5 = \alpha - 1.62\beta$$

The cyclopentadienyl carbonium ion is predicted to be a diradical having π-electronic energy

$$E_{C_5H_5(+)} = 4\alpha + 5.24\beta$$

while the cyclopentadienyl radical has energy

$$E_{C_5H_5(\cdot)} = 5\alpha + 5.85\beta$$

The total energy of the six electrons present in the anion is found to be:

$$E_{C_5H_5(-)} = 6\alpha + 6.47\beta$$

The results are diagrammatically presented in Figure 3–16.

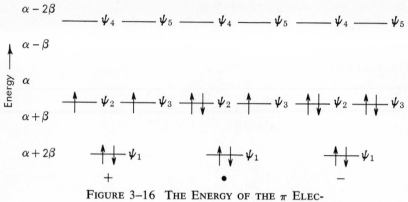

$\alpha - 2\beta$ ——— ψ_4 ——— ψ_5 ——— ψ_4 ——— ψ_5 ——— ψ_4 ——— ψ_5

$\alpha - \beta$

α

$\alpha + \beta$ —↑— ψ_2 —↑— ψ_3 —↑↓— ψ_2 —↑— ψ_3 —↑↓— ψ_2 —↑↓— ψ_3

$\alpha + 2\beta$ —↑↓— ψ_1 —↑↓— ψ_1 —↑↓— ψ_1

+   •   —

FIGURE 3–16 THE ENERGY OF THE π ELEC-
TRONS IN THE CYCLOPENTADIENYL SYSTEM

In the cyclopropenyl system the carbonium ion was calculated to be much more stable than the anion. Here, the situation is reversed. In proceeding from the carbonium ion to the carbanion the stability of the materials increases. The carbanion obeys Hückel's rule with n equal to 1.

6.8. HEXATRIENE

$$C_1 - C_2 - C_3 - C_4 - C_5 - C_6$$

$$\psi = a_1 p_1 + a_2 p_2 + a_3 p_3 + a_4 p_4 + a_5 p_5 + a_6 p_6$$

$$\begin{vmatrix} H_{11} - S_{11}E & H_{12} - S_{12}E & H_{13} - S_{13}E & H_{14} - S_{14}E & H_{15} - S_{15}E & H_{16} - S_{16}E \\ H_{21} - S_{21}E & H_{22} - S_{22}E & H_{23} - S_{23}E & H_{24} - S_{24}E & H_{25} - S_{25}E & H_{26} - S_{26}E \\ H_{31} - S_{31}E & H_{32} - S_{32}E & H_{33} - S_{33}E & H_{34} - S_{34}E & H_{35} - S_{35}E & H_{36} - S_{36}E \\ H_{41} - S_{41}E & H_{42} - S_{42}E & H_{43} - S_{43}E & H_{44} - S_{44}E & H_{45} - S_{45}E & H_{46} - S_{46}E \\ H_{51} - S_{51}E & H_{52} - S_{52}E & H_{53} - S_{53}E & H_{54} - S_{54}E & H_{55} - S_{55}E & H_{56} - S_{56}E \\ H_{61} - S_{61}E & H_{62} - S_{62}E & H_{63} - S_{63}E & H_{64} - S_{64}E & H_{65} - S_{65}E & H_{66} - S_{66}E \end{vmatrix} = 0$$

Rewritten in terms of x this becomes

$$\begin{vmatrix} x & 1 & 0 & 0 & 0 & 0 \\ 1 & x & 1 & 0 & 0 & 0 \\ 0 & 1 & x & 1 & 0 & 0 \\ 0 & 0 & 1 & x & 1 & 0 \\ 0 & 0 & 0 & 1 & x & 1 \\ 0 & 0 & 0 & 0 & 1 & x \end{vmatrix} = 0$$

and

$$x \begin{vmatrix} x & 1 & 0 & 0 & 0 \\ 1 & x & 1 & 0 & 0 \\ 0 & 1 & x & 1 & 0 \\ 0 & 0 & 1 & x & 1 \\ 0 & 0 & 0 & 1 & x \end{vmatrix} - 1 \begin{vmatrix} 1 & 1 & 0 & 0 & 0 \\ 0 & x & 1 & 0 & 0 \\ 0 & 1 & x & 1 & 0 \\ 0 & 0 & 1 & x & 1 \\ 0 & 0 & 0 & 1 & x \end{vmatrix} = 0$$

Expanding further

$$x^2 \begin{vmatrix} x & 1 & 0 & 0 \\ 1 & x & 1 & 0 \\ 0 & 1 & x & 1 \\ 0 & 0 & 1 & x \end{vmatrix} - x \begin{vmatrix} 1 & 1 & 0 & 0 \\ 0 & x & 1 & 0 \\ 0 & 1 & x & 1 \\ 0 & 0 & 1 & x \end{vmatrix} - 1 \begin{vmatrix} x & 1 & 0 & 0 \\ 1 & x & 1 & 0 \\ 0 & 1 & x & 1 \\ 0 & 0 & 1 & x \end{vmatrix} + 1 \begin{vmatrix} 0 & 1 & 0 & 0 \\ 0 & x & 1 & 0 \\ 0 & 1 & x & 1 \\ 0 & 0 & 1 & x \end{vmatrix} = 0$$

The last determinant in this equation equals zero. Expanding the others in terms of third-order determinants

$$x^3 \begin{vmatrix} x & 1 & 0 \\ 1 & x & 1 \\ 0 & 1 & x \end{vmatrix} - x^2 \begin{vmatrix} 1 & 1 & 0 \\ 0 & x & 1 \\ 0 & 1 & x \end{vmatrix} - x \begin{vmatrix} x & 1 & 0 \\ 1 & x & 1 \\ 0 & 1 & x \end{vmatrix}$$

$$+ x \begin{vmatrix} 0 & 1 & 0 \\ 0 & x & 1 \\ 0 & 1 & x \end{vmatrix} - x \begin{vmatrix} x & 1 & 0 \\ 1 & x & 1 \\ 0 & 1 & x \end{vmatrix} + 1 \begin{vmatrix} 1 & 1 & 0 \\ 0 & x & 1 \\ 0 & 1 & x \end{vmatrix} = 0$$

Further development of the above leads to the following polynomial equation:

$$x^6 - 5x^4 + 6x^2 - 1 = 0$$

which has the roots,

$$x = -1.80, \quad x = -1.25, \quad x = -0.445, \quad x = 0.445,$$
$$x = 1.25, \quad x = 1.80$$

$$x = -1.80$$
$$E_1 = \alpha + 1.80\beta$$

$$x = -1.25$$
$$E_2 = \alpha + 1.25\beta$$

$$x = -0.445$$

$$E_3 = \alpha + 0.445\beta$$

$$x = 0.445$$

$$E_4 = \alpha - 0.445\beta$$

$$x = 1.25$$

$$E_5 = \alpha - 1.25\beta$$

$$x = 1.80$$

$$E_6 = \alpha - 1.80\beta$$

The six electrons are placed in the three bonding molecular orbitals (see Figure 3–17).

$$E = 6\alpha + 6.99\beta$$

and

$$\text{resonance energy} = -0.99\beta$$

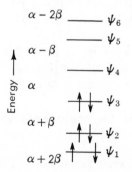

FIGURE 3–17   THE ENERGY OF THE SIX π-ELECTRONS IN HEXATRIENE

6.9.   BENZENE

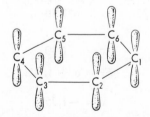

$$\psi = a_1 p_1 + a_2 p_2 + a_3 p_3 + a_4 p_4 + a_5 p_5 + a_6 p_6$$

$$\begin{vmatrix} H_{11}-S_{11}E & H_{12}-S_{12}E & H_{13}-S_{13}E & H_{14}-S_{14}E & H_{15}-S_{15}E & H_{16}-S_{16}E \\ H_{21}-S_{21}E & H_{22}-S_{22}E & H_{23}-S_{23}E & H_{24}-S_{24}E & H_{25}-S_{25}E & H_{26}-S_{26}E \\ H_{31}-S_{31}E & H_{32}-S_{32}E & H_{33}-S_{33}E & H_{34}-S_{34}E & H_{35}-S_{35}E & H_{36}-S_{36}E \\ H_{41}-S_{41}E & H_{42}-S_{42}E & H_{43}-S_{43}E & H_{44}-S_{44}E & H_{45}-S_{45}E & H_{46}-S_{46}E \\ H_{51}-S_{51}E & H_{52}-S_{52}E & H_{53}-S_{53}E & H_{54}-S_{54}E & H_{55}-S_{55}E & H_{56}-S_{56}E \\ H_{61}-S_{61}E & H_{62}-S_{62}E & H_{63}-S_{63}E & H_{64}-S_{64}E & H_{65}-S_{65}E & H_{66}-S_{66}E \end{vmatrix} = 0$$

or

$$\begin{vmatrix} x & 1 & 0 & 0 & 0 & 1 \\ 1 & x & 1 & 0 & 0 & 0 \\ 0 & 1 & x & 1 & 0 & 0 \\ 0 & 0 & 1 & x & 1 & 0 \\ 0 & 0 & 0 & 1 & x & 1 \\ 1 & 0 & 0 & 0 & 1 & x \end{vmatrix} = 0$$

Expanding

$$x\begin{vmatrix} x & 1 & 0 & 0 & 0 \\ 1 & x & 1 & 0 & 0 \\ 0 & 1 & x & 1 & 0 \\ 0 & 0 & 1 & x & 1 \\ 0 & 0 & 0 & 1 & x \end{vmatrix} - 1\begin{vmatrix} 1 & 1 & 0 & 0 & 0 \\ 0 & x & 1 & 0 & 0 \\ 0 & 1 & x & 1 & 0 \\ 0 & 0 & 1 & x & 1 \\ 1 & 0 & 0 & 1 & x \end{vmatrix}$$

$$- 1\begin{vmatrix} 1 & x & 1 & 0 & 0 \\ 0 & 1 & x & 1 & 0 \\ 0 & 0 & 1 & x & 1 \\ 0 & 0 & 0 & 1 & x \\ 1 & 0 & 0 & 0 & 1 \end{vmatrix} = 0$$

Then

$$x^2\begin{vmatrix} x & 1 & 0 & 0 \\ 1 & x & 1 & 0 \\ 0 & 1 & x & 1 \\ 0 & 0 & 1 & x \end{vmatrix} - x\begin{vmatrix} 1 & 1 & 0 & 0 \\ 0 & x & 1 & 0 \\ 0 & 1 & x & 1 \\ 0 & 0 & 1 & x \end{vmatrix} - 1\begin{vmatrix} x & 1 & 0 & 0 \\ 1 & x & 1 & 0 \\ 0 & 1 & x & 1 \\ 0 & 0 & 1 & x \end{vmatrix}$$

$$+ 1\begin{vmatrix} 0 & 1 & 0 & 0 \\ 0 & x & 1 & 0 \\ 0 & 1 & x & 1 \\ 1 & 0 & 1 & x \end{vmatrix} - 1\begin{vmatrix} 1 & x & 1 & 0 \\ 0 & 1 & x & 1 \\ 0 & 0 & 1 & x \\ 0 & 0 & 0 & 1 \end{vmatrix}$$

$$+ x\begin{vmatrix} 0 & x & 1 & 0 \\ 0 & 1 & x & 1 \\ 0 & 0 & 1 & x \\ 1 & 0 & 0 & 1 \end{vmatrix} - 1\begin{vmatrix} 0 & 1 & 1 & 0 \\ 0 & 0 & x & 1 \\ 0 & 0 & 1 & x \\ 1 & 0 & 0 & 1 \end{vmatrix} = 0$$

In terms of third-order determinants we have

$$x^3 \begin{vmatrix} x & 1 & 0 \\ 1 & x & 1 \\ 0 & 1 & x \end{vmatrix} - x^2 \begin{vmatrix} 1 & 1 & 0 \\ 0 & x & 1 \\ 0 & 1 & x \end{vmatrix} - x \begin{vmatrix} x & 1 & 0 \\ 1 & x & 1 \\ 0 & 1 & x \end{vmatrix}$$

$$+ x \begin{vmatrix} 0 & 1 & 0 \\ 0 & x & 1 \\ 0 & 1 & x \end{vmatrix} - x \begin{vmatrix} x & 1 & 0 \\ 1 & x & 1 \\ 0 & 1 & x \end{vmatrix} + 1 \begin{vmatrix} 1 & 1 & 0 \\ 0 & x & 1 \\ 0 & 1 & x \end{vmatrix}$$

$$- 1 \begin{vmatrix} 0 & 1 & 0 \\ 0 & x & 1 \\ 1 & 1 & x \end{vmatrix} - 1 \begin{vmatrix} 1 & x & 1 \\ 0 & 1 & x \\ 0 & 0 & 1 \end{vmatrix} + x \begin{vmatrix} 0 & x & 1 \\ 0 & 1 & x \\ 0 & 0 & 1 \end{vmatrix}$$

$$- 1 \begin{vmatrix} 0 & 1 & 1 \\ 0 & 0 & x \\ 0 & 0 & 1 \end{vmatrix} - x^2 \begin{vmatrix} 0 & x & 1 \\ 0 & 1 & x \\ 1 & 0 & 1 \end{vmatrix} + x \begin{vmatrix} 0 & 1 & 1 \\ 0 & 0 & x \\ 1 & 0 & 1 \end{vmatrix}$$

$$+ 1 \begin{vmatrix} 0 & x & 1 \\ 0 & 1 & x \\ 1 & 0 & 1 \end{vmatrix} - 1 \begin{vmatrix} 0 & 0 & 1 \\ 0 & 0 & x \\ 1 & 0 & 1 \end{vmatrix} = 0$$

and

$$x^6 - 6x^4 + 9x^2 - 4 = 0$$

which has the roots

$$x = -2, \quad x = -1, \quad x = -1, \quad x = 1, \quad x = 1, \quad x = 2$$

$$x = -2$$
$$E_1 = \alpha + 2\beta$$

$$x = -1$$
$$E_2 = \alpha + \beta$$

$$x = -1$$
$$E_3 = \alpha + \beta$$

$$x = 1$$
$$E_4 = \alpha - \beta$$

$$x = 1$$
$$E_5 = \alpha - \beta$$

$$x = 2$$
$$E_6 = \alpha - 2\beta$$

All bonding orbitals are complete, and the total energy is

$$E = 6\alpha + 8\beta$$

resonance energy $= -2\beta$

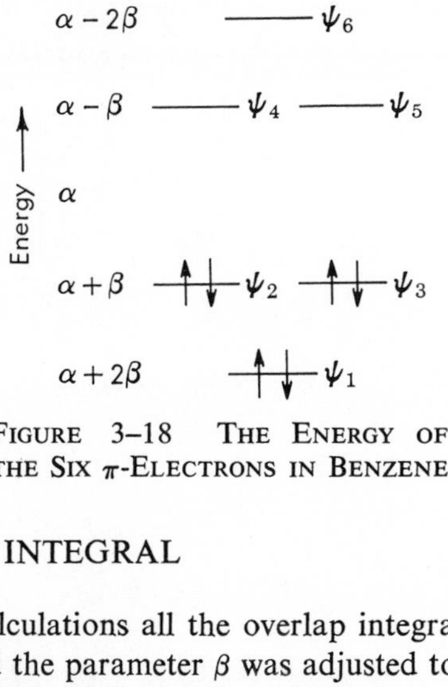

FIGURE 3–18 THE ENERGY OF
THE SIX π-ELECTRONS IN BENZENE

7. THE OVERLAP INTEGRAL

In our previous calculations all the overlap integrals, S_{AB} $A \neq B$, were set equal to zero, and the parameter β was adjusted to take this simplification into account. While satisfactory results are obtained in this manner the value of these integrals is certainly not zero. They are a measure of the overlap between the p_z orbitals in question, and as bonding is usually considered to result from orbital overlap, we naturally expect some value other than zero for these integrals. In fact, for benzene the overlap integral between adjacent carbon atoms has a value of 0.25.[30] Some of the more rigorous molecular-orbital methods include overlap between adjacent atoms, and some calculations have even included overlap between non-adjacent atoms though this is less common. Another approach that may be employed in a more rigorous treatment is to construct atomic orbitals that

---

[30] R. S. Mulliken, C. A. Rieke, D. Orloff, and H. Orloff, *J. Chem. Phys.*, **17**, 1248 (1949).

actually are orthogonal.[31] These orthogonal atomic orbitals are linear combinations of the usual atomic orbitals and are formed in such a way that all integrals of the type S_{AB}, $A \neq B$, are zero.

Of course, inclusion of overlap in a calculation changes the energy levels of the various molecular orbitals. As an example let us re-evaluate the secular equation for ethylene and include overlap between the orbitals in our calculation. The secular equation is:

$$\begin{vmatrix} H_{11} - S_{11}E & H_{12} - S_{12}E \\ H_{21} - S_{21}E & H_{22} - S_{22}E \end{vmatrix} = 0$$

When overlap is included, the terms H_{12} and H_{21} that were previously given the symbol β are now represented by the symbol γ. The various energy states of the electron are expressed in terms of the parameters α and γ. We make the following substitutions:

$$H_{11} = H_{22} = \alpha$$

$$H_{12} = H_{21} = \gamma$$

$$S_{11} = S_{22} = 1$$

$$S_{12} = S_{21} = S$$

and our secular determinant becomes:

$$\begin{vmatrix} \alpha - E & \gamma - SE \\ \gamma - SE & \alpha - E \end{vmatrix} = 0$$

Dividing through by $\gamma - SE$ and letting $x = (\alpha - E)/(\gamma - SE)$, we obtain

$$\begin{vmatrix} x & 1 \\ 1 & x \end{vmatrix} = 0$$

which has the same solutions as before, $x = \pm 1$. However, x now stands for a different quantity. Substituting for $x = -1$,

$$\frac{\alpha - E_1}{\gamma - SE_1} = -1$$

---

[31] P. O. Löwdin, *Advan. in Phys.*, **5**, 1 (1956).

or

$$\alpha - E_1 = -\gamma + SE_1$$

$$\alpha + \gamma = E_1 + SE_1$$

then

$$E_1 = \frac{\alpha + \gamma}{1 + S}$$

If

$$x = 1$$

then

$$\frac{\alpha - E_2}{\gamma - SE_2} = 1$$

and

$$E_2 = \frac{\alpha - \gamma}{1 - S}$$

The new energy levels for our molecular orbitals are:

$$E_1 = \frac{\alpha + \gamma}{1 + S}$$

$$E_2 = \frac{\alpha - \gamma}{1 - S}$$

Notice that if we allow S to equal zero and replace γ by β, we obtain our previous result.

Once again we are interested in comparing the energies of the various molecular orbitals. The simplest way to make this comparison when overlap is included is to define α, the energy of an electron in a p_z atomic orbital, as the zero of energy. Setting $\alpha = 0$,

$$E_1 = \frac{\gamma}{1 + S}$$

$$E_2 = \frac{-\gamma}{1 - S}$$

Now, the value of S is not constant but a function of the distance separating the carbon atoms. In ethylene this distance is 1.33 A. Nevertheless, the value of S usually chosen in such calculations is 0.25, the value in benzene. Employing this value of S,

$$E_1 = 0.80\gamma$$

$$E_2 = -1.3\gamma$$

Whereas, in our previous calculation the two energy levels were symmetrically displaced from α, $\alpha \pm \beta$, these new molecular orbitals are not symmetrical about zero. The results are schematically illustrated in Figure 3–19.

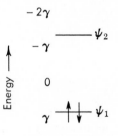

FIGURE 3–19   THE ENERGY OF THE TWO π-ELECTRONS IN ETHYLENE WITH OVERLAP INCLUDED

PROBLEMS

1. Derive the equation

$$a_1(H_{21} - S_{21}E) + a_2(H_{22} - S_{22}E) = 0$$

   See equation (3.16); remember that $H_{12} = H_{21}$ and $S_{12} = S_{21}$.
2. Calculate the excitation energy for ethylene, butadiene, and hexatriene. Is the calculated ease of excitation in agreement with your expectations?
3. Calculate the resonance energy of the cyclopentadienyl radical and anion.
4. Calculate the total π-electronic energy and the resonance energy of the following:

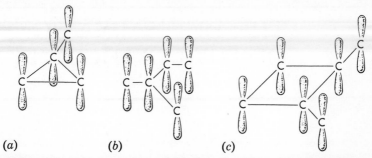

(a)   (b)   (c)

In problem 4b carry out the calculation for the carbonium ion, radical, and carbanion. Save the results of problem 4. See Chapter 4, problem 6.

Chapter Four

THE DETERMINATION
OF THE COEFFICIENTS

1. NORMALIZATION REQUIREMENT

In Chapter 3, having expressed a molecular orbital as a linear combination of atomic orbitals, the energy of several molecular systems was determined. At that time the coefficients a_1, a_2, a_3, ... a_n were neglected. We shall now evaluate them. There is a general requirement that our coefficients must satisfy. This requirement stems from the consideration of our molecular orbitals as an orthonormal set.

$$\int \psi_A \psi_B \, dv = \begin{cases} 1 & A = B \\ 0 & A \neq B \end{cases} \qquad (4.1)$$

As an example, a molecular orbital of ethylene is given by:

$$\psi = a_1 p_1 + a_2 p_2 \qquad (4.2)$$

and normalization requires that:

$$\int \psi \psi \, dv = 1$$

Substitution of equation (4.2) into this expression yields:

$$\int (a_1 p_1 + a_2 p_2)(a_1 p_1 + a_2 p_2) \, dv = 1$$

or

$$a_1{}^2 \int p_1p_1 \, dv + 2a_1a_2 \int p_1p_2 \, dv + a_2{}^2 \int p_2p_2 \, dv = 1 \qquad (4.3)$$

(Remember that $\int p_1p_2 \, dv = \int p_2p_1 \, dv$.)

Now, our p atomic orbitals also form an orthonormal set (see equation 3.6).

$$\int p_A p_B \, dv = \begin{cases} 1 & A = B \\ 0 & A \neq B \end{cases}$$

In light of this condition, equation (4.3) becomes:

$$a_1{}^2 + a_2{}^2 = 1$$

This is the normalization requirement for ethylene. For a system of n atomic orbitals,

$$\psi = a_1p_1 + a_2p_2 + a_3p_3 + \cdots + a_np_n$$

and our general normalization requirement becomes:

$$a_1{}^2 + a_2{}^2 + a_3{}^2 + \cdots + a_n{}^2 = 1 \qquad (4.4)$$

The sum of the squares of the coefficients must equal unity.

Here, we have one equation involving the coefficients. Using either the homogeneous equations or the secular equation (Chapter 3, section 5), we are able to express all other coefficients in terms of a_1. Substituting these expressions into equation (4.4), we can solve for a_1 and consequently for all coefficients. We illustrate using ethylene as the first example.

2. ETHYLENE

The two homogeneous linear equations for ethylene are given by expression (3.16) as:

$$a_1(H_{11} - S_{11}E) + a_2(H_{12} - S_{12}E) = 0$$

$$a_1(H_{21} - S_{21}E) + a_2(H_{22} - S_{22}E) = 0$$

where:

$$H_{11} = H_{22} = \alpha$$

$$H_{12} = H_{21} = \beta$$

$$S_{11} = S_{22} = 1$$

$$S_{12} = S_{21} = 0$$

Substitution of these quantities into these homogeneous equations affords:

$$a_1(\alpha - E) + a_2\beta \qquad = 0$$

$$a_1\beta \qquad + a_2(\alpha - E) = 0$$

Upon division of both of these equations by β, we obtain:

$$a_1\left(\frac{\alpha - E}{\beta}\right) + a_2 \qquad = 0$$

$$a_1 \qquad + a_2\left(\frac{\alpha - E}{\beta}\right) = 0$$

Now let

$$x = \frac{\alpha - E}{\beta}$$

then,

$$a_1x + a_2 = 0$$

$$a_1 + a_2x = 0 \qquad\qquad (4.5)$$

Expression (4.5) may also be obtained from the secular equation for ethylene (see equations 3.18 and 3.19). The complete equation is:

$$a_1 \cdot a_2 \begin{vmatrix} H_{11} - S_{11}E & H_{12} - S_{12}E \\ H_{21} - S_{21}E & H_{22} - S_{22}E \end{vmatrix} = 0$$

Since,

$$a_1\, a_2 \neq 0$$

the secular determinant must equal zero.

$$\begin{vmatrix} H_{11} - S_{11}E & H_{12} - S_{12}E \\ H_{21} - S_{21}E & H_{22} - S_{22}E \end{vmatrix} = 0$$

Including the coefficients again and placing them inside the determinant, we get:

$$\begin{vmatrix} a_1(H_{11} - S_{11}E) & a_2(H_{12} - S_{12}E) \\ a_1(H_{21} - S_{21}E) & a_2(H_{22} - S_{22}E) \end{vmatrix} = 0$$

and in terms of x this becomes:

$$\begin{vmatrix} a_1x & a_2 \\ a_1 & a_2x \end{vmatrix} = 0$$

We can rewrite this equation as a pair of homogeneous linear equations and obtain (4.5).

$$a_1x + a_2 = 0$$

$$a_1 + a_2x = 0$$

The bonding molecular orbital ψ_1 of ethylene has energy $\alpha + \beta$. To find the coefficients, a_1 and a_2, corresponding to this molecular orbital, we use expression (4.5) relating the coefficients as well as the normalization requirement, which for ethylene is:

$$a_1{}^2 + a_2{}^2 = 1 \tag{4.6}$$

The value of x corresponding to ψ_1 is -1. For it is when x equals -1 that the energy of the molecular orbital is $\alpha + \beta$. To determine the proper values of a_1 and a_2, we substitute $x = -1$ into expression (4.5), and we find that

$$a_2 = a_1$$

Therefore,

$$a_2{}^2 = a_1{}^2$$

Having found a_2 in terms of a_1, it is possible to solve for a_1 using the normalization requirement. Substitution of the term a_1^2 for its equivalent, a_2^2, yields:

$$a_1^2 + a_1^2 = 1$$

or

$$a_1 = \frac{1}{\sqrt{2}}$$

We shall always keep a_1 positive. Furthermore,

$$a_2 = a_1$$

$$a_2 = \frac{1}{\sqrt{2}}$$

The normalized eigenfunction for the bonding molecular orbital of ethylene is:

$$\psi_1 = \frac{1}{\sqrt{2}}p_1 + \frac{1}{\sqrt{2}}p_2 \tag{4.7}$$

For the case $x = 1$, we find that

$$a_2 = -a_1$$

which still leads to

$$a_2^2 = a_1^2$$

The value of a_1 is determined once again from the normalization requirement.

$$a_1 = \frac{1}{\sqrt{2}}$$

but now,

$$a_2 = -a_1$$

$$a_2 = -\frac{1}{\sqrt{2}}$$

and the normalized eigenfunction is:

$$\psi_2 = \frac{1}{\sqrt{2}}p_1 - \frac{1}{\sqrt{2}}p_2 \tag{4.8}$$

This is the antibonding eigenfunction of energy E_2, $\alpha - \beta$. The two molecular orbitals for ethylene take the form,

$$\psi_1 = \frac{1}{\sqrt{2}}(p_1 + p_2)$$

$$\psi_2 = \frac{1}{\sqrt{2}}(p_1 - p_2)$$

These are plotted in Figure 4–1 below. Now, p_1 and p_2 are the p_z orbitals on carbon atoms 1 and 2 respectively, and the value of p_1 is small except near C_1. Similarly, p_2 is small except in the region near C_2. First we plot ψ_1 the bonding molecular orbital. Starting at the origin and approaching C_1, ψ is small until we are close to C_1. Near carbon atom 1 the value of p_1 becomes large and ψ increases, attaining its maximum value at C_1. Passing carbon atom 1, p_1 decreases in value and ψ falls off, but now, the value of p_2 becomes significant. The value of ψ is appreciable even between the carbon atoms, for we are adding p_1 and p_2 and their sum is large. As we

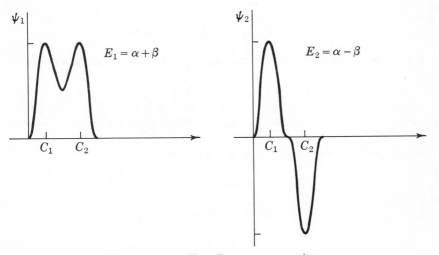

FIGURE 4–1   THE BONDING AND ANTI-
BONDING EIGENFUNCTIONS FOR ETHYLENE

approach C_2, ψ again increases. Its second maximum occurs at C_2. Past C_2, it falls in value and rapidly becomes negligible.

The situation is similar for the antibonding molecular orbital until we pass C_1. From this point on, not only does p_1 decrease in value, but we are subtracting the value of p_2. Therefore, ψ falls off very rapidly after passing C_1 and becomes zero midway between the carbon atoms where the value of p_1 equals that of p_2. After this, ψ becomes negative for now p_2 is larger than p_1. At C_2, ψ has its minimum. After that p_2 decreases and ψ again approaches zero.

3. THE ALLYL SYSTEM

For the allyl system normalization requires that for each molecular orbital

$$a_1{}^2 + a_2{}^2 + a_3{}^2 = 1$$

The secular equation is:

$$\begin{vmatrix} x & 1 & 0 \\ 1 & x & 1 \\ 0 & 1 & x \end{vmatrix} = 0$$

which has the roots

$$x = -\sqrt{2}, \qquad x = 0, \qquad x = \sqrt{2}$$

Reincorporation of the coefficients a_1, a_2, a_3 into the determinant yields:

$$\begin{vmatrix} a_1x & a_2 & 0 \\ a_1 & a_2x & a_3 \\ 0 & a_2 & a_3x \end{vmatrix} = 0$$

which can be written as three linear equations.

$$a_1x + a_2 \qquad\qquad = 0$$

$$a_1 \ + a_2x + a_3 \ = 0$$

$$a_2 \ + a_3x = 0 \qquad\qquad (4.9)$$

First, let us determine the values of the coefficients for the bonding molecular orbital ψ_1. For this case $x = -\sqrt{2}$, and we have

$$-\sqrt{2}a_1 + \quad a_2 \quad\quad\quad = 0$$

$$a_1 - \sqrt{2}a_2 + \quad a_3 = 0$$

$$a_2 - \sqrt{2}a_3 = 0$$

The first of these equations gives us a_2 in terms of a_1.

$$a_2 = \sqrt{2}a_1 \tag{4.10}$$

The third equation gives a_3 in terms of a_2. Substitution of (4.10) gives a_3 in terms of a_1.

$$\sqrt{2}a_3 = a_2$$

or

$$a_3 = a_1$$

Since

$$a_1{}^2 + \quad a_2{}^2 + a_3{}^2 = 1$$

we have

$$a_1{}^2 + 2a_1{}^2 + a_1{}^2 = 1$$

Then

$$a_1{}^2 = \frac{1}{4}$$

$$a_1 = \frac{1}{2}$$

and

$$a_2 = \frac{\sqrt{2}}{2} \quad \text{(see 4.10)}$$

$$a_3 = \frac{1}{2}$$

Therefore,

$$\psi_1 = \frac{1}{2}p_1 + \frac{\sqrt{2}}{2}p_2 + \frac{1}{2}p_3$$

For the case $x = 0$ expression (4.9) becomes

$$a_2 \qquad = 0$$

$$a_1 \qquad + a_3 = 0$$

$$a_2 \qquad = 0$$

Therefore,

$$a_1 = a_1$$

$$a_2 = 0$$

$$a_3 = -a_1$$

and normalization now requires that

$$a_1{}^2 + a_1{}^2 = 1$$

or

$$a_1 = \frac{1}{\sqrt{2}}$$

$$a_2 = 0$$

$$a_3 = -\frac{1}{\sqrt{2}}$$

and

$$\psi_2 = \frac{1}{\sqrt{2}}p_1 - \frac{1}{\sqrt{2}}p_3$$

For $x = \sqrt{2}$,

$$\sqrt{2}a_1 + \quad a_2 \quad\quad\quad = 0$$

$$a_1 + \sqrt{2}a_2 + \quad a_3 = 0$$

$$a_2 + \sqrt{2}a_3 = 0$$

and we find that

$$a_2 = -\sqrt{2}a_1$$

$$a_3 = \quad a_1$$

Since

$$a_1{}^2 + 2a_1{}^2 + a_1{}^2 = 1$$

$$a_1 = \frac{1}{2}$$

$$a_2 = -\frac{\sqrt{2}}{2}$$

$$a_3 = \frac{1}{2}$$

$$\psi_3 = \frac{1}{2}p_1 - \frac{\sqrt{2}}{2}p_2 + \frac{1}{2}p_3$$

The three eigenfunctions are:

$$\psi_1 = \frac{1}{2}(p_1 + \sqrt{2}p_2 + p_3)$$

$$\psi_2 = \frac{1}{\sqrt{2}}(p_1 - p_3)$$

$$\psi_3 = \frac{1}{2}(p_1 - \sqrt{2}p_2 + p_3)$$

We plot these eigenfunctions in Figure 4–2.

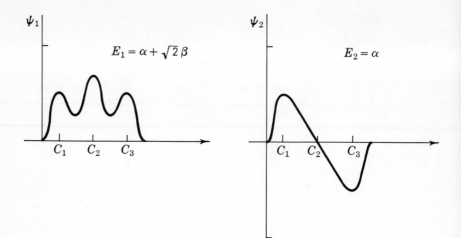

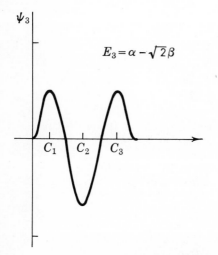

FIGURE 4–2 THE BONDING, NONBONDING, AND ANTI-BONDING EIGENFUNCTIONS FOR THE ALLYL SYSTEM

4. THE CYCLOPROPENYL SYSTEM

The secular equation for this system is:

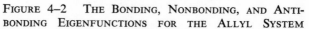

$$\begin{vmatrix} x & 1 & 1 \\ 1 & x & 1 \\ 1 & 1 & x \end{vmatrix} = 0$$

Upon reintroduction of the coefficients, this leads to the following equations:

$$a_1x + a_2 + a_3 = 0$$
$$a_1 + a_2x + a_3 = 0$$
$$a_1 + a_2 + a_3x = 0$$

The roots of the determinant were found to be:

$$x = -2, \qquad x = 1, \qquad x = 1$$

$$x = -2$$

$$-2a_1 + a_2 + a_3 = 0$$
$$a_1 - 2a_2 + a_3 = 0$$
$$a_1 + a_2 - 2a_3 = 0$$

To find a_2 in terms of a_1 we subtract the second of these equations from the first one. This results in the following:

$$-3a_1 + 3a_2 = 0$$

$$a_2 = a_1$$

To find a_3 in terms of a_1 we subtract the third equation from the first.

$$-3a_1 + 3a_3 = 0$$

$$a_3 = a_1$$

Turning to the normalization requirement,

$$a_1{}^2 + a_2{}^2 + a_3{}^2 = 1$$

Substituting the appropriate expressions yields:

$$a_1 = \frac{1}{\sqrt{3}}$$

$$a_2 = \frac{1}{\sqrt{3}}$$

$$a_3 = \frac{1}{\sqrt{3}}$$

$$\psi_1 = \frac{1}{\sqrt{3}}p_1 + \frac{1}{\sqrt{3}}p_2 + \frac{1}{\sqrt{3}}p_3$$

$$x = 1$$

$$a_1 + a_2 + a_3 = 0$$

$$a_1 + a_2 + a_3 = 0$$

$$a_1 + a_2 + a_3 = 0 \qquad (4.11)$$

For the first time we encounter some difficulty in obtaining the coefficients. In the case of degenerate orbitals, here ψ_2 and ψ_3 are degenerate, molecular-orbital theory does not allow us to determine the coefficients uniquely. We are free to choose any values for the coefficients a_1, a_2, a_3 of ψ_2 provided the orthonormality requirement and expression (4.11) are simultaneously satisfied. The fact that the ψ's must be orthogonal requires that for ψ_2,

$$\int \psi_1 \psi_2 \, dv = 0$$

and

$$\int \psi_3 \psi_2 \, dv = 0$$

Since we may choose any values for a_1, a_2, a_3, one simple way to satisfy all requirements is to set one of the coefficients in expression (4.11) equal to zero. Let us set a_2 equal to zero. Then

$$a_1 = a_1$$

$$a_2 = 0$$

$$a_3 = -a_1$$

Normalization implies that

$$a_1^2 + a_2^2 + a_3^2 = 1$$

or

$$a_1^2 + 0 \ \ + a_1^2 = 1$$

Now

$$a_1 = \frac{1}{\sqrt{2}}$$

$$a_2 = 0$$

$$a_3 = -\frac{1}{\sqrt{2}}$$

and we find that one possible expression for ψ_2 is:

$$\psi_2 = \frac{1}{\sqrt{2}}p_1 - \frac{1}{\sqrt{2}}p_3$$

To determine ψ_3, substitution of $x = 1$ which is the appropriate value of x for ψ_3 again leads to (4.11). However, having chosen ψ_2, we are no longer free to choose the coefficients for ψ_3. These are dictated by the fact that ψ_3 must be orthogonal to ψ_1 and ψ_2.

$$\int \psi_1 \psi_3 \, dv = 0$$

$$\int \psi_2 \psi_3 \, dv = 0$$

We need consider only the orthogonality to ψ_2.
    Since

$$\psi_3 = a_1 p_1 + a_2 p_2 + a_3 p_3$$

orthogonality to ψ_2 leads to:

$$\int \frac{1}{\sqrt{2}}(p_1 - p_3)(a_1 p_1 + a_2 p_2 + a_3 p_3) \, dv = 0$$

Remember that

$$\int p_A p_B \, dv = \begin{cases} 1 & A = B \\ 0 & A \neq B \end{cases}$$

then,

$$\frac{1}{\sqrt{2}}a_1 - \frac{1}{\sqrt{2}}a_3 = 0$$

and

$$a_3 = a_1$$

Having found a_3, to find a_2 in terms of a_1 we return to (4.11). Since $a_3 = a_1$, expression (4.11) becomes:

$$a_1 + a_2 + a_1 = 0$$

or

$$a_2 = -2a_1$$

Thus for ψ_3,

$$a_1 = a_1$$

$$a_2 = -2a_1$$

$$a_3 = a_1$$

Since normalization requires that

$$a_1{}^2 + a_2{}^2 + a_3{}^2 = 1$$

for ψ_3,

and
$$a_1{}^2 + 4a_1{}^2 + a_1{}^2 = 1$$

$$a_1 = \frac{1}{\sqrt{6}}$$

$$a_2 = -\frac{2}{\sqrt{6}}$$

$$a_3 = \frac{1}{\sqrt{6}}$$

$$\psi_3 = \frac{1}{\sqrt{6}}p_1 - \frac{2}{\sqrt{6}}p_2 + \frac{1}{\sqrt{6}}p_3$$

The three eigenfunctions, as shown in Figure 4–3, for the cyclopropenyl system are:

$$\psi_1 = \frac{1}{\sqrt{3}}(p_1 + p_2 + p_3)$$

$$\psi_2 = \frac{1}{\sqrt{2}}(p_1 - p_3)$$

$$\psi_3 = \frac{1}{\sqrt{6}}(p_1 - 2p_2 + p_3)$$

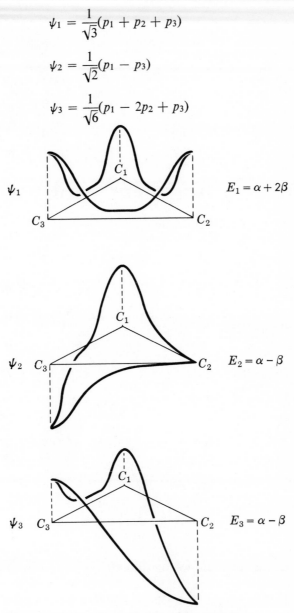

ψ_1 $E_1 = \alpha + 2\beta$

ψ_2 $E_2 = \alpha - \beta$

ψ_3 $E_3 = \alpha - \beta$

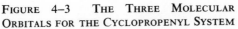

FIGURE 4–3   THE THREE MOLECULAR
ORBITALS FOR THE CYCLOPROPENYL SYSTEM

5. BUTADIENE

In terms of x the four linear homogeneous equations for butadiene take the form:

$$a_1x + a_2 \qquad\qquad\qquad = 0$$

$$a_1 \;+\; a_2x + a_3 \qquad\qquad = 0$$

$$a_2 \;+\; a_3x + a_4 \;=\; 0$$

$$a_3 \;+\; a_4x = 0 \qquad\qquad (4.12)$$

where

$$x = -1.62, \qquad -0.618, \qquad 0.618, \qquad 1.62$$

For ψ_1, $x = -1.62$, and we obtain

$$-1.62a_1 + \qquad a_2 \qquad\qquad\qquad = 0$$

$$a_1 - 1.62a_2 + \qquad a_3 \qquad\qquad = 0$$

$$a_2 - 1.62a_3 + \qquad a_4 = 0$$

$$a_3 - 1.62a_4 = 0$$

The first equation yields,

$$a_2 = 1.62a_1$$

Substitution of this value for a_2 into the second equation gives:

$$a_1 - 1.62(1.62a_1) + a_3 = 0$$

or

$$a_3 = 1.62a_1$$

From the last equation, we substitute for a_3 in terms of a_1 and obtain:

$$1.62a_1 - 1.62a_4 = 0$$

$$a_4 = a_1$$

We must normalize the eigenfunction.

$$a_1{}^2 + a_2{}^2 + a_3{}^2 + a_4{}^2 = 1$$

Making the appropriate substitutions,

$$a_1{}^2 + 2.62a_1{}^2 + 2.62a_1{}^2 + a_1{}^2 = 1$$

$$a_1 = \frac{1}{\sqrt{7.24}}$$

$$a_1 = 0.372$$

$$a_2 = 0.602$$

$$a_3 = 0.602$$

$$a_4 = 0.372$$

and

$$\psi_1 = 0.372p_1 + 0.602p_2 + 0.602p_3 + 0.372p_4$$

To obtain the coefficients for ψ_2 we use the value of x, $x = -0.618$, and carry out the same procedure that is illustrated above. The results are:

$$a_2 = 0.618a_1$$

$$a_3 = -0.618a_1$$

$$a_4 = -a_1$$

and

$$a_1{}^2 + 0.382a_1{}^2 + 0.382a_1{}^2 + a_1{}^2 = 1$$

$$a_1 = \frac{1}{\sqrt{2.76}}$$

$$a_1 = 0.602$$

$$a_2 = 0.372$$

$$a_3 = -0.372$$

$$a_4 = -0.602$$

$$\psi_2 = 0.602p_1 + 0.372p_2 - 0.372p_3 - 0.602p_4$$

Using the values $x = 0.618$ and 1.62, this same procedure is repeated for ψ_3 and ψ_4. The four eigenfunctions (see Figure 4–4) for butadiene are:

$$\psi_1 = 0.372p_1 + 0.602p_2 + 0.602p_3 + 0.372p_3$$
$$\psi_2 = 0.602p_1 + 0.372p_2 - 0.372p_3 - 0.602p_4$$
$$\psi_3 = 0.602p_1 - 0.372p_2 - 0.372p_3 + 0.602p_4$$
$$\psi_4 = 0.372p_1 - 0.602p_2 + 0.602p_3 - 0.372p_4$$

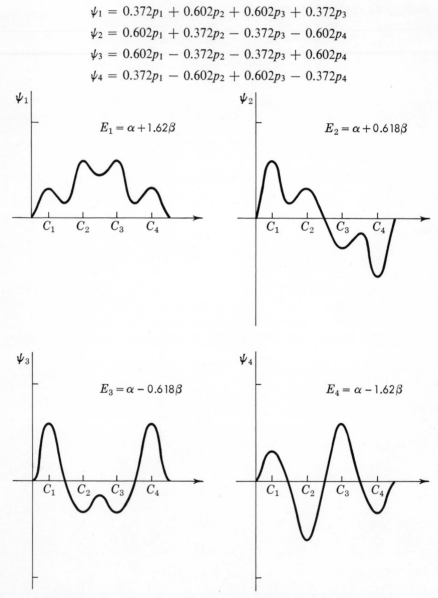

FIGURE 4–4   THE FOUR MOLECULAR ORBITALS FOR BUTADIENE

6. GAUSS'S METHOD OF ELIMINATION

Up to this point the procedure used to evaluate the coefficients has been fairly straightforward, but the examples have been simple. We shall now develop a method for solving systems of linear equations that is more general and quite rapid. In fact, this method, Gauss's *method of elimination*, is perhaps the best general technique, and it is the one commonly employed for solving these equations on computers.

Two systems of equations are said to be equivalent if all solutions of one system are solutions of the other. Gauss's method involves the transformation of a set of equations into equivalent sets. As an example, let us consider the case of cyclobutadiene.

7. CYCLOBUTADIENE

The homogeneous equations for cyclobutadiene when written in terms of x become:

$$a_1x + a_2 \qquad\;\; + a_4 = 0$$

$$a_1 + a_2x + a_3 \qquad = 0$$

$$a_2 + a_3x + a_4 = 0$$

$$a_1 \qquad + a_3 + a_4x = 0 \qquad\qquad (4.13)$$

where x takes on the permissible values, $x = -2, 0, 0, 2$.

$$x = -2$$

$$-2a_1 + a_2 \qquad\;\; + a_4 = 0$$

$$a_1 - 2a_2 + a_3 \qquad = 0$$

$$a_2 - 2a_3 + a_4 = 0$$

$$a_1 \qquad + a_3 - 2a_4 = 0$$

Here we have a system of simultaneous equations that must be satisfied, and we are seeking to express a_2, a_3, and a_4 in terms of a_1. We shall eliminate the term a_2 from all equations but the first, the term a_3 from all equations but the second, and the term a_4 from all equations but the third.

Equation one contains a_2 and is kept unaltered. In order to eliminate a_2 from the second equation we multiply the first by two and add them.

$$-4a_1 + 2a_2 \qquad + 2a_4 = 0$$

$$a_1 - 2a_2 + a_3 \qquad = 0$$

$$\overline{-3a_1 \qquad + a_3 + 2a_4 = 0}$$

This gives us two equations, the original first one and this new one.

$$-2a_1 + a_2 \qquad + a_4 = 0$$

$$-3a_1 \qquad + a_3 + 2a_4 = 0$$

To eliminate a_2 from the third equation we subtract it from the first.

$$-2a_1 + a_2 \qquad + a_4 = 0$$

$$a_2 - 2a_3 + a_4 = 0$$

$$\overline{-2a_1 \qquad + 2a_3 \qquad = 0}$$

We have already found a_3 in terms of a_1, but let us neglect this result and continue in systematic fashion. Equation four does not contain a_2 and is kept unaltered. We now have the following system of equations:

$$-2a_1 + a_2 \qquad + a_4 = 0$$

$$-3a_1 \qquad + a_3 + 2a_4 = 0$$

$$-2a_1 \qquad + 2a_3 \qquad = 0$$

$$a_1 \qquad + a_3 - 2a_4 = 0 \qquad (4.14)$$

This set of equations is equivalent to the original set but has the advantage that a_2 occurs only in equation one. Working with this second set, (4.14) we proceed to eliminate a_3 from all but the second equation. Equation one (4.14) does not contain a_3, and we want to keep a_3 in equation two. These two equations are not changed. To remove the term a_3 from equation three, we multiply the second equation by two and subtract the third.

$$-6a_1 \qquad + 2a_3 + 4a_4 = 0$$
$$-2a_1 \qquad + 2a_3 \qquad = 0$$

$$\overline{\,-4a_1 \qquad\qquad\quad + 4a_4 = 0}$$

To eliminate a_3 from equation four, we subtract it from equation two.

$$-3a_1 \qquad + \; a_3 + 2a_4 = 0$$

$$a_1 \qquad + \; a_3 - 2a_4 = 0$$

$$\overline{\,-4a_1 \qquad\qquad\quad + 4a_4 = 0}$$

This gives us another equivalent set.

$$-2a_1 + a_2 \qquad\quad + \; a_4 = 0$$

$$-3a_1 \qquad + \; a_3 + 2a_4 = 0$$

$$-4a_1 \qquad\qquad\quad + 4a_4 = 0$$

$$-4a_1 \qquad\qquad\quad + 4a_4 = 0 \qquad\qquad (4.15)$$

We have eliminated a_2 from all but the first equation in (4.15) and a_3 from all but the second. Let us eliminate a_4 from all but the third. To accomplish this, we multiply equation one (4.15) by four and subtract equation three from it.

$$-8a_1 + 4a_2 \qquad\quad + 4a_4 = 0$$

$$-4a_1 \qquad\qquad\quad + 4a_4 = 0$$

$$\overline{\,-4a_1 + 4a_2 \qquad\qquad\quad = 0}$$

To eliminate a_4 from equation two, we multiply it by two and subtract equation three.

$$-6a_1 \qquad + 2a_3 + 4a_4 = 0$$

$$-4a_1 \qquad\qquad\quad + 4a_4 = 0$$

$$\overline{\,-2a_1 \qquad + 2a_3 \qquad = 0}$$

Equation three is kept unchanged, and equation four is identical to equation three so we retain it also. This gives us our final equivalent set.

$$-4a_1 + 4a_2 \qquad\qquad\qquad = 0$$

$$-2a_1 \qquad\quad + 2a_3 \qquad\quad = 0$$

$$-4a_1 \qquad\qquad\quad + 4a_4 = 0$$

$$-4a_1 \qquad\qquad\quad + 4a_4 = 0 \qquad (4.16)$$

Expression (4.16) represents a system of equations that is equivalent to our original system, yet it allows us to obtain directly the desired coefficients in terms of a_1. We find that:

$$a_2 = a_1$$

$$a_3 = a_1$$

and

$$a_4 = a_1$$

Substitution into the normalization requirement yields:

$$a_1 = \tfrac{1}{2}$$

$$a_2 = \tfrac{1}{2}$$

$$a_3 = \tfrac{1}{2}$$

$$a_4 = \tfrac{1}{2}$$

and

$$\psi_1 = \tfrac{1}{2}p_1 + \tfrac{1}{2}p_2 + \tfrac{1}{2}p_3 + \tfrac{1}{2}p_4$$

It is clear that this systematic process can be extended and applied to systems of any size. Suitable manipulation of the original set of linear equations yields an equivalent set that contains a_2 only in equation one, a_3 only in equation two, a_4 only in equation three, and so forth.

Let us return to the homogeneous equations, (4.13), for cyclobutadiene and evaluate the coefficients for ψ_2 and ψ_3. Gauss's method is not necessary here. These two molecular orbitals are degenerate, and a procedure similar to that employed in the treatment of the cyclopropenyl system must be used.

When x is equal to zero, expression (4.13) becomes:

$$a_2 \qquad + a_4 = 0$$

$$a_1 \qquad + a_3 \qquad = 0$$

$$a_2 \qquad + a_4 = 0$$

$$a_1 \qquad + a_3 \qquad = 0 \qquad (4.17)$$

Resulting in the fact that for both ψ_2 and ψ_3,

$$a_1 = -a_3$$

and

$$a_2 = -a_4$$

We are free to choose any values for the coefficients of ψ_2 which satisfy both (4.17) and the orthonormality requirement. We set a_2 equal to zero. Then for ψ_2,

$$a_1 = a_1$$

$$a_2 = 0$$

$$a_3 = -a_1$$

$$a_4 = 0$$

Normalization of ψ_2 requires that the value of a_1 be $1/\sqrt{2}$, and

$$a_2 = 0$$

$$a_3 = -\frac{1}{\sqrt{2}}$$

$$a_4 = 0$$

Therefore,

$$\psi_2 = \frac{1}{\sqrt{2}}p_1 - \frac{1}{\sqrt{2}}p_3$$

The coefficients of ψ_3 are found from expression (4.17) and from its orthogonality to ψ_2.

$$\psi_3 = a_1 p_1 + a_2 p_2 + a_3 p_3 + a_4 p_4$$

and

$$\int \psi_2 \psi_3 \, dv = 0$$

Evaluation of the coefficients for ψ_3 subject to these restrictions gives rise to

$$a_1 = 0$$

$$a_2 = \frac{1}{\sqrt{2}}$$

$$a_3 = 0$$

$$a_4 = -\frac{1}{\sqrt{2}}$$

Thus,

$$\psi_3 = \frac{1}{\sqrt{2}} p_2 - \frac{1}{\sqrt{2}} p_4$$

To evaluate ψ_4 from the homogeneous equations, we make the substitution $x = 2$, and in this case, these equations become:

$$2a_1 + a_2 \qquad + a_4 = 0$$

$$a_1 + 2a_2 + a_3 \qquad = 0$$

$$a_2 + 2a_3 + a_4 = 0$$

$$a_1 \qquad + a_3 + 2a_4 = 0$$

It is possible to use the method of elimination. The procedure is the same as that employed for ψ_1, and one obtains as the values of the coefficients,

$$a_1 = \tfrac{1}{2}$$

$$a_2 = -\tfrac{1}{2}$$

$$a_3 = \tfrac{1}{2}$$

$$a_4 = -\tfrac{1}{2}$$

The four orthonormal eigenfunctions for cyclobutadiene are illustrated (see Figure 4–5):

$$\psi_1 = \frac{1}{2}(p_1 + p_2 + p_3 + p_4)$$

$$\psi_2 = \frac{1}{\sqrt{2}}(p_1 - p_3)$$

$$\psi_3 = \frac{1}{\sqrt{2}}(p_2 - p_4)$$

$$\psi_4 = \frac{1}{2}(p_1 - p_2 + p_3 - p_4)$$

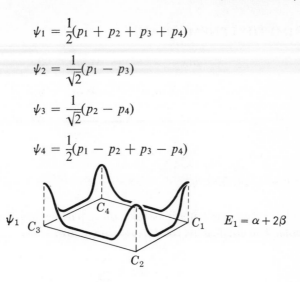

ψ_1 $E_1 = \alpha + 2\beta$

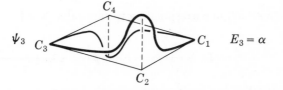

ψ_2 $E_2 = \alpha$

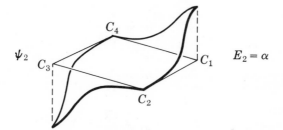

ψ_3 $E_3 = \alpha$

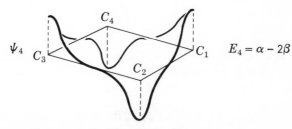

ψ_4 $E_4 = \alpha - 2\beta$

FIGURE 4–5 THE FOUR EIGEN-
FUNCTIONS FOR CYCLOBUTADIENE

8. TRIMETHYLENEMETHANE

$$a_1 x \qquad\qquad + a_4 = 0$$

$$a_2 x \qquad + a_4 = 0$$

$$a_3 x + a_4 = 0$$

$$a_1 + a_2 + a_3 + a_4 x = 0$$

where $x = -\sqrt{3}, 0, 0, \sqrt{3}$

The homogeneous equations take on a particularly easy form for this molecule. The coefficients for ψ_1, $x = -\sqrt{3}$, are:

$$a_1 = \frac{1}{\sqrt{6}}$$

$$a_2 = \frac{1}{\sqrt{6}}$$

$$a_3 = \frac{1}{\sqrt{6}}$$

$$a_4 = \frac{\sqrt{3}}{\sqrt{6}}$$

and the eigenfunction corresponding to this value of x is:

$$\psi_1 = \frac{1}{\sqrt{6}}(p_1 + p_2 + p_3 + \sqrt{3}p_4)$$

For ψ_2, $x = 0$, we are required to set a_4 equal to zero. Let us also set a_2 equal to zero. Then,

$$a_1 = a_1$$

$$a_2 = 0$$

$$a_3 = -a_1$$

$$a_4 = 0$$

and

$$\psi_2 = \frac{1}{\sqrt{2}}(p_1 - p_3)$$

For the case of ψ_3, we have:

$$a_1 = a_1$$

$$a_2 = -2a_1$$

$$a_3 = a_1$$

$$a_4 = 0$$

Therefore,

$$\psi_3 = \frac{1}{\sqrt{6}}(p_1 - 2p_2 + p_3)$$

Finally, we make the substitution, $x = \sqrt{3}$, and find that for ψ_4,

$$a_1 = a_1$$

$$a_2 = a_1$$

$$a_3 = a_1$$

$$a_4 = -\sqrt{3}a_1$$

and

$$\psi_4 = \frac{1}{\sqrt{6}}(p_1 + p_2 + p_3 - \sqrt{3}p_4)$$

The four molecular orbitals for trimethylenemethane are:

$$\psi_1 = \frac{1}{\sqrt{6}}(p_1 + p_2 + p_3 + \sqrt{3}p_4)$$

$$\psi_2 = \frac{1}{\sqrt{2}}(p_1 - p_3)$$

$$\psi_3 = \frac{1}{\sqrt{6}}(p_1 - 2p_2 + p_3)$$

$$\psi_4 = \frac{1}{\sqrt{6}}(p_1 + p_2 + p_3 - \sqrt{3}p_4)$$

9. THE CYCLOPENTADIENYL SYSTEM

$$a_1 x + a_2 \qquad\qquad\quad + a_5 = 0$$
$$a_1 \ + a_2 x + a_3 \qquad\qquad\quad = 0$$
$$a_2 \ + a_3 x + a_4 \qquad\quad = 0$$
$$a_3 \ + a_4 x + a_5 = 0$$
$$a_1 \qquad\qquad\quad + a_4 \ + a_5 x = 0$$

where x may take on the values -2.00, -0.618, -0.618, 1.62, 1.62.

We shall evaluate the coefficients for ψ_1 using the method of elimination. The simultaneous equations become:

$$-2a_1 + \ a_2 \qquad\qquad\quad + \ a_5 = 0$$
$$a_1 - 2a_2 + \ a_3 \qquad\qquad = 0$$
$$a_2 - 2a_3 + \ a_4 \qquad = 0$$
$$a_3 - 2a_4 + \ a_5 = 0$$
$$a_1 \qquad\qquad\quad + \ a_4 - 2a_5 = 0$$

We proceed to find an equivalent set of equations that contains a_2 only in the first equation of the set. Multiplying equation one by two and adding the second equation yields:

$$-3a_1 \qquad\quad + \ a_3 \qquad + 2a_5 = 0$$

We eliminate a_2 from the third by subtracting it from equation one.

$$-2a_1 \qquad + 2a_3 - \ a_4 + \ a_5 = 0$$

Equations four and five do not contain a_2 and remain unchanged. We have found a new system of equations having the desired property.

$$-2a_1 + a_2 \qquad\qquad\quad + \ a_5 = 0$$
$$-3a_1 \qquad\quad + \ a_3 \qquad + 2a_5 = 0$$
$$-2a_1 \qquad\quad + 2a_3 - \ a_4 + \ a_5 = 0$$
$$a_3 - 2a_4 + \ a_5 = 0$$
$$a_1 \qquad\qquad\quad + \ a_4 - 2a_5 = 0$$

The original first, fourth, and fifth equations are kept plus the two new ones. Working with this new set, we eliminate a_3 from all equations but the second. This results in the following:

$$-2a_1 + a_2 \qquad\qquad + a_5 = 0$$

$$-3a_1 \qquad + a_3 \qquad + 2a_5 = 0$$

$$-4a_1 \qquad\qquad + a_4 + 3a_5 = 0$$

$$-3a_1 \qquad\qquad + 2a_4 + a_5 = 0$$

$$a_1 \qquad\qquad + a_4 - 2a_5 = 0$$

Eliminating a_4 from all but the third,

$$-2a_1 + a_2 \qquad\qquad + a_5 = 0$$

$$-3a_1 \qquad + a_3 \qquad + 2a_5 = 0$$

$$-4a_1 \qquad\qquad + a_4 + 3a_5 = 0$$

$$-5a_1 \qquad\qquad + 5a_5 = 0$$

$$-5a_1 \qquad\qquad + 5a_5 = 0$$

The fourth and fifth equations are identical. We eliminate a_5 from the first three.

$$-5a_1 + 5a_2 \qquad\qquad\qquad = 0$$

$$-5a_1 \qquad + 5a_3 \qquad\qquad = 0$$

$$-5a_1 \qquad\qquad + 5a_4 \qquad = 0$$

$$-5a_1 \qquad\qquad\qquad + 5a_5 = 0$$

$$-5a_1 \qquad\qquad\qquad + 5a_5 = 0$$

Using the values obtained for the coefficients, we find that

$$\psi_1 = \frac{1}{\sqrt{5}}(p_1 + p_2 + p_3 + p_4 + p_5)$$

The other four eigenfunctions are present as degenerate pairs. We set a_5 equal to zero in ψ_2, and evaluate the coefficients of ψ_2 and ψ_3 accordingly.

Application of the same technique to ψ_4 and ψ_5 completes the solution. The five molecular orbitals for the cyclopentadienyl system are:

$$\psi_1 = \frac{1}{\sqrt{5}}(p_1 + p_2 + p_3 + p_4 + p_5)$$

$$\psi_2 = 0.602p_1 + 0.372p_2 - 0.372p_3 - 0.602p_4$$

$$\psi_3 = 0.196p_1 - 0.512p_2 - 0.512p_3 + 0.196p_4 + 0.633p_5$$

$$\psi_4 = 0.372p_1 - 0.602p_2 + 0.602p_3 - 0.372p_4$$

$$\psi_5 = 0.512p_1 - 0.196p_2 - 0.196p_3 + 0.512p_4 - 0.633p_5$$

10. HEXATRIENE

For hexatriene the homogeneous linear equations when written in terms of x take the form

$$
\begin{aligned}
a_1x + a_2 &= 0 \\
a_1 + a_2x + a_3 &= 0 \\
a_2 + a_3x + a_4 &= 0 \\
a_3 + a_4x + a_5 &= 0 \\
a_4 + a_5x + a_6 &= 0 \\
a_5 + a_6x &= 0
\end{aligned}
$$

and x takes on the values -1.80, -1.25, -0.445, 0.445, 1.25, 1.80. The six eigenfunctions that correspond to these values of x are:

$$\psi_1 = 0.233p_1 + 0.419p_2 + 0.521p_3 + 0.521p_4 + 0.419p_5 + 0.233p_6$$

$$\psi_2 = 0.419p_1 + 0.521p_2 + 0.233p_3 - 0.233p_4 - 0.521p_5 - 0.419p_6$$

$$\psi_3 = 0.521p_1 + 0.233p_2 - 0.419p_3 - 0.419p_4 + 0.233p_5 + 0.521p_6$$

$$\psi_4 = 0.521p_1 - 0.233p_2 - 0.419p_3 + 0.419p_4 + 0.233p_5 - 0.521p_6$$

$$\psi_5 = 0.419p_1 - 0.521p_2 + 0.233p_3 + 0.233p_4 - 0.521p_5 + 0.419p_6$$

$$\psi_6 = 0.233p_1 - 0.419p_2 + 0.521p_3 - 0.521p_4 + 0.419p_5 - 0.233p_6$$

11. BENZENE

$$a_1x + a_2 \qquad\qquad\qquad + a_6 \;= 0$$

$$a_1 \;+ a_2x + a_3 \qquad\qquad\qquad\quad = 0$$

$$a_2 \;+ a_3x + a_4 \qquad\qquad\quad = 0$$

$$a_3 \;+ a_4x + a_5 \qquad\quad = 0$$

$$a_4 \;+ a_5x + a_6 \;= 0$$

$$a_1 \qquad\qquad\qquad\qquad + a_5 \;+ a_6x = 0$$

For benzene, x takes on the very nice values -2, -1, -1, 1, 1, 2, and the six molecular orbitals that are found upon substitution of these values for x into the homogeneous equations are:

$$\psi_1 = \frac{1}{\sqrt{6}}(p_1 + p_2 + p_3 + p_4 + p_5 + p_6)$$

$$\psi_2 = \frac{1}{2}(p_1 + p_2 - p_4 - p_5)$$

$$\psi_3 = \frac{1}{\sqrt{12}}(p_1 - p_2 - 2p_3 - p_4 + p_5 + 2p_6)$$

$$\psi_4 = \frac{1}{2}(p_1 - p_2 + p_4 - p_5)$$

$$\psi_5 = \frac{1}{\sqrt{12}}(p_1 + p_2 - 2p_3 + p_4 + p_5 - 2p_6)$$

$$\psi_6 = \frac{1}{\sqrt{6}}(p_1 - p_2 + p_3 - p_4 + p_5 - p_6)$$

12. THE PRINCIPLE OF SUPERPOSITION

Let us consider the two simple eigenfunctions

$$\psi_A = \sin^2 x$$

$$\psi_B = \cos^2 x$$

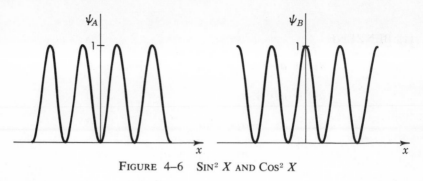

FIGURE 4–6   SIN² X AND COS² X

These functions are illustrated in Figure 4–6.

One possible superposition of these two functions is their sum.

$$\psi = \psi_A + \psi_B$$

$$\psi = \sin^2 x + \cos^2 x$$

$$\psi = 1$$

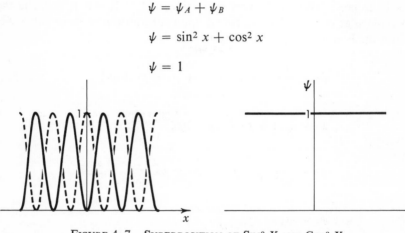

FIGURE 4–7   SUPERPOSITION OF SIN² X AND COS² X

This is shown in Figure 4–7. At each and every point x, we add the values of ψ_A and ψ_B. The result is the straight line $\psi = 1$. A superposition of functions is merely their linear combination. A more general description of the superposition of two functions ψ_A and ψ_B is given by the expression

$$\psi = a\psi_A + b\psi_B$$

This concept plays a role in both valence-bond and molecular-orbital theory. In valence-bond theory, a molecule is considered to be a superposition of the various valence-bond structures. We shall discuss this idea more fully in Chapter 7. In molecular-orbital theory, it comes into play in connection with degenerate molecular orbitals.

If two molecular orbitals ψ_A and ψ_B are degenerate, then a new molecular orbital ψ formed as a linear combination of ψ_A and ψ_B also corresponds to the same eigenvalue (energy). We have

$$H\psi_A = E\psi_A$$

and

$$H\psi_B = E\psi_B \qquad (4.18)$$

and we wish to show that ψ also has energy E, that is,

$$H\psi = E\psi$$

where

$$\psi = a\psi_A + b\psi_B$$

Multiplying the first equation in (4.18) by a and the second by b gives:

$$aH\psi_A = aE\psi_A$$

$$bH\psi_B = bE\psi_B$$

Since a and b are numbers, these equations may be rewritten as:

$$Ha\psi_A = Ea\psi_A$$

$$Hb\psi_B = Eb\psi_B$$

Summing the two,

$$Ha\psi_A + Hb\psi_B = Ea\psi_A + Eb\psi_B$$

or

$$H(a\psi_A + b\psi_B) = E(a\psi_A + b\psi_B)$$

The expression in parenthesis is ψ, and this gives:

$$H\psi = E\psi$$

Given two degenerate molecular orbitals, we may make an infinite number of new molecular orbitals, all corresponding to the same energy as the original two. Thus, when dealing with degenerate molecular orbitals such as in the case of the cyclopropenyl and cyclopentadienyl systems, we were able to choose any values for the coefficients. This gave us just one out of an infinite number of possible molecular orbitals. However, having picked one molecular orbital of the degenerate pair, it was required that the other be orthogonal. Returning to the case of the cyclopropenyl system, the two degenerate molecular orbitals were found to be:

$$\psi_2 = \frac{1}{\sqrt{2}}(p_1 - p_3)$$

$$\psi_3 = \frac{1}{\sqrt{6}}(p_1 - 2p_2 + p_3)$$

Let us arbitrarily construct a new molecular orbital

$$\psi_A = \frac{1}{2}\psi_2 + \frac{\sqrt{3}}{2}\psi_3$$

then

$$\psi_A = \frac{1}{2\sqrt{2}}p_1 - \frac{1}{2\sqrt{2}}p_3 + \frac{1}{2\sqrt{2}}p_1 - \frac{1}{\sqrt{2}}p_2 + \frac{1}{2\sqrt{2}}p_3$$

$$\psi_A = \frac{1}{\sqrt{2}}p_1 - \frac{1}{\sqrt{2}}p_2$$

or

$$\psi_A = \frac{1}{\sqrt{2}}(p_1 - p_2)$$

We have a new molecular orbital ψ_A that is degenerate with both ψ_2 and ψ_3. We can form still another linear combination of ψ_2 and ψ_3.

$$\psi_B = \frac{\sqrt{3}}{2}\psi_2 - \frac{1}{2}\psi_3$$

$$\psi_B = \frac{\sqrt{3}}{2\sqrt{2}}p_1 - \frac{\sqrt{3}}{2\sqrt{2}}p_3 - \frac{1}{2\sqrt{6}}p_1 + \frac{1}{\sqrt{6}}p_2 - \frac{1}{2\sqrt{6}}p_3$$

$$\psi_B = \frac{1}{\sqrt{6}}p_1 + \frac{1}{\sqrt{6}}p_2 - \frac{2}{\sqrt{6}}p_3$$

or

$$\psi_B = \frac{1}{\sqrt{6}}(p_1 + p_2 - 2p_3)$$

This results in still another eigenfunction that is degenerate with both of the original molecular orbitals and also with ψ_A. These two new eigenfunctions are just as good a representation of the electrons as are the previous two, and all pertinent data such as electron density, charge density, and so forth, remain the same as before. Furthermore, ψ_A and ψ_B are orthogonal to each other and to ψ_1:

$$\psi_1 = \frac{1}{\sqrt{3}}(p_1 + p_2 + p_3)$$

$$\psi_A = \frac{1}{\sqrt{2}}(p_1 - p_2)$$

$$\psi_B = \frac{1}{\sqrt{6}}(p_1 + p_2 - 2p_3)$$

PROBLEMS

1. Verify that the four eigenfunctions for butadiene are orthogonal.
2. Show that all the molecular orbitals of benzene are normalized.
3. (a) Sketch the molecular orbitals of hexatriene.
   (b) Sketch the new molecular orbitals for the cyclopropenyl system. Compare these with the original set illustrated in Figure 4–3.
4. Verify that ψ_3 for cyclobutadiene takes the form given in section 4-7.
5. Construct two new eigenfunctions, using ψ_2 and ψ_3 of benzene, which are a linear combination of these two degenerate eigenfunctions.
6. Determine the coefficients for all of the molecular orbitals of the following three systems (see problem 4, Chapter 3).

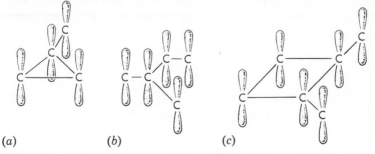

(a)   (b)   (c)

Save the results of problem 6 for Chapter 3, problem 3.

Chapter Five

ELECTRON DENSITY, CHARGE DENSITY, BOND ORDER AND FREE VALENCE

1. ELECTRON DENSITY

1.1. Consider one of the two electrons in the π bond of ethylene. The molecular orbital associated with this electron is

$$\psi_1 = a_1 p_1 + a_2 p_2 \qquad (5.1)$$

where

$$a_1 = a_2 = \frac{1}{\sqrt{2}}$$

In Chapter 2, section 3, the idea was brought forth that the probability of finding this electron in the volume element dv, alternatively the electron density in that volume element, is given by the value of $\psi_1{}^2\, dv$ and that the total electron density is given by

$$\int \psi_1 \psi_1 \, dv = 1$$

Upon substitution of equation (5.1) this becomes,

$$\int \psi_1 \psi_1 \, dv = a_1{}^2 + a_2{}^2 = 1$$

The total electron density due to one electron is given by the sum of the squares of the coefficients (see equation 4.4). We are interested in the electron density at each of the two carbon atoms of ethylene. At carbon atom 1 this is equal to $a_1{}^2$ and at carbon atom 2, $a_2{}^2$. We have one electron that has an electron density at C_1 equal to

$$a_1{}^2 = \left(\frac{1}{\sqrt{2}}\right)^2$$

$$a_1{}^2 = \frac{1}{2}$$

and at C_2,

$$a_2{}^2 = \left(\frac{1}{\sqrt{2}}\right)^2$$

$$a_2{}^2 = \frac{1}{2}$$

Since there are two π-electrons occupying this orbital in ethylene, the electron density at C_1 (ED_1) due to both of these electrons is

$$ED_1 = 2(\tfrac{1}{2})$$

$$= 1.00$$

at C_2,

$$ED_2 = 2(\tfrac{1}{2})$$

$$= 1.00$$

As we might expect, we find an electron density of one at each carbon atom, making both of these atoms neutral. The electron density generated at some carbon atom C_A by one π-electron in a given orbital is equal to the square of the coefficient $a_A{}^2$ for that orbital.

1.2. THE ALLYL SYSTEM   In the allyl carbonium ion both π-electrons are in ψ_1 which is given by the expression

$$\psi_1 = \frac{1}{2}p_1 + \frac{\sqrt{2}}{2}p_2 + \frac{1}{2}p_3$$

The electron density at each position due to one electron in ψ_1 equals

$$\text{at } C_1 = \; (\tfrac{1}{2})^2 \; = \frac{1}{4}$$

$$\text{at } C_2 = \left(\frac{\sqrt{2}}{2}\right)^2 = \frac{1}{2}$$

$$\text{at } C_3 = \; (\tfrac{1}{2})^2 \; = \frac{1}{4}$$

There are two π-electrons in the allyl carbonium ion, and we find for the total electron density at C_1, C_2, and C_3,

$$ED_1 = 2(\tfrac{1}{4}) = 0.500$$

$$ED_2 = 2(\tfrac{1}{2}) = 1.00$$

$$ED_3 = 2(\tfrac{1}{4}) = 0.500$$

In the allyl radical we have two electrons in ψ_1 and one electron in ψ_2.

$$\psi_1 = \frac{1}{2}p_1 + \frac{\sqrt{2}}{2}p_2 + \frac{1}{2}p_3$$

$$\psi_2 = \frac{1}{\sqrt{2}}p_1 - \frac{1}{\sqrt{2}}p_3$$

The electron density at carbon atom 1 due to the two electrons in ψ_1 is equal to $2(\tfrac{1}{2})^2$ and that due to the one electron in ψ_2 is equal to $(1/\sqrt{2})^2$. The electron density at carbon atoms 2 and 3 is calculated in similar fashion. The value of a_2 in the second molecular orbital ψ_2 is zero. Consequently, the electron density at each position is:

$$ED_1 = \; 2(\tfrac{1}{2})^2 + \left(\frac{1}{\sqrt{2}}\right)^2 \; = 1.00$$

$$ED_2 = \; 2\left(\frac{\sqrt{2}}{2}\right)^2 + (0)^2 \; = 1.00$$

$$ED_3 = 2(\tfrac{1}{2})^2 + \left(-\frac{1}{\sqrt{2}}\right)^2 = 1.00$$

The carbanion has two electrons in ψ_1 and two in ψ_2, and we find that

$$ED_1 = 2(\tfrac{1}{2})^2 + 2\left(\frac{1}{\sqrt{2}}\right)^2 = 1.50$$

$$ED_2 = 2\left(\frac{\sqrt{2}}{2}\right)^2 + 2(0)^2 = 1.00$$

$$ED_3 = 2(\tfrac{1}{2})^2 + 2\left(\frac{-1}{\sqrt{2}}\right)^2 = 1.50$$

1.3. THE CYCLOPROPENYL SYSTEM The three eigenfunctions for this system are:

$$\psi_1 = \frac{1}{\sqrt{3}}p_1 + \frac{1}{\sqrt{3}}p_2 + \frac{1}{\sqrt{3}}p_3$$

$$\psi_2 = \frac{1}{\sqrt{2}}p_1 - \frac{1}{\sqrt{2}}p_3$$

$$\psi_3 = \frac{1}{\sqrt{6}}p_1 - \frac{2}{\sqrt{6}}p_2 + \frac{1}{\sqrt{6}}p_3$$

For the carbonium ion we find:

$$ED_1 = 2\left(\frac{1}{\sqrt{3}}\right)^2 = \frac{2}{3}$$

$$ED_2 = 2\left(\frac{1}{\sqrt{3}}\right)^2 = \frac{2}{3}$$

$$ED_3 = 2\left(\frac{1}{\sqrt{3}}\right)^2 = \frac{2}{3}$$

The cyclopropenyl carbanion has two electrons in ψ_1, one electron in ψ_2, and one in ψ_3. The electron density at each carbon atom is:

$$ED_1 = 2\left(\frac{1}{\sqrt{3}}\right)^2 + \left(\frac{1}{\sqrt{2}}\right)^2 + \left(\frac{1}{\sqrt{6}}\right)^2 = 1\tfrac{1}{3}$$

$$ED_2 = 2\left(\frac{1}{\sqrt{3}}\right)^2 + (0)^2 + \left(\frac{-2}{\sqrt{6}}\right)^2 = 1\tfrac{1}{3}$$

$$ED_3 = 2\left(\frac{1}{\sqrt{3}}\right)^2 + \left(\frac{-1}{\sqrt{2}}\right)^2 + \left(\frac{1}{\sqrt{6}}\right)^2 = 1\tfrac{1}{3}$$

1.4. BUTADIENE

$$\psi_1 = 0.372p_1 + 0.602p_2 + 0.602p_3 + 0.372p_4$$

$$\psi_2 = 0.602p_1 + 0.372p_2 - 0.372p_3 - 0.602p_4$$

With two electrons in both ψ_1 and ψ_2 the total electron density is calculated to be:

$$ED_1 = 2(0.372)^2 + 2(0.602)^2 \quad = 1.00$$

$$ED_2 = 2(0.602)^2 + 2(0.372)^2 \quad = 1.00$$

$$ED_3 = 2(0.602)^2 + 2(-0.372)^2 = 1.00$$

$$ED_4 = 2(0.372)^2 + 2(-0.602)^2 = 1.00$$

Notice that the electron density for the entire molecule equals four ($ED_1 + ED_2 + ED_3 + ED_4$), which is as it should be. There are four π-electrons in butadiene.

1.5. BENZENE

In benzene the three bonding molecular orbitals are full.

$$\psi_1 = \frac{1}{\sqrt{6}}p_1 + \frac{1}{\sqrt{6}}p_2 + \frac{1}{\sqrt{6}}p_3 + \frac{1}{\sqrt{6}}p_4 + \frac{1}{\sqrt{6}}p_5 + \frac{1}{\sqrt{6}}p_6$$

$$\psi_2 = \frac{1}{2}p_1 + \frac{1}{2}p_2 - \frac{1}{2}p_4 - \frac{1}{2}p_5$$

$$\psi_3 = \frac{1}{\sqrt{12}}p_1 - \frac{1}{\sqrt{12}}p_2 - \frac{2}{\sqrt{12}}p_3 - \frac{1}{\sqrt{12}}p_4 + \frac{1}{\sqrt{12}}p_5 + \frac{2}{\sqrt{12}}p_6$$

and

$$ED_1 = 2\left(\frac{1}{\sqrt{6}}\right)^2 + 2\left(\frac{1}{2}\right)^2 + 2\left(\frac{1}{\sqrt{12}}\right)^2 = 1.00$$

$$ED_2 = 2\left(\frac{1}{\sqrt{6}}\right)^2 + 2\left(\frac{1}{2}\right)^2 + 2\left(\frac{-1}{\sqrt{12}}\right)^2 = 1.00$$

$$ED_3 = 2\left(\frac{1}{\sqrt{6}}\right)^2 + 2(0)^2 + 2\left(\frac{-2}{\sqrt{12}}\right)^2 = 1.00$$

$$ED_4 = 2\left(\frac{1}{\sqrt{6}}\right)^2 + 2\left(-\frac{1}{2}\right)^2 + 2\left(\frac{-1}{\sqrt{12}}\right)^2 = 1.00$$

$$ED_5 = 2\left(\frac{1}{\sqrt{6}}\right)^2 + 2\left(-\frac{1}{2}\right)^2 + 2\left(\frac{1}{\sqrt{12}}\right)^2 = 1.00$$

$$ED_6 = 2\left(\frac{1}{\sqrt{6}}\right)^2 + 2(0)^2 + 2\left(\frac{2}{\sqrt{12}}\right)^2 = 1.00$$

In general, to obtain the electron density at some position, say C_A, we square the coefficient of p_A in all occupied orbitals, multiply each of these terms by a number equal to the occupation number (1 or 2) of that orbital, and sum them,

$$ED_A = \sum a_{Aa_A}$$

where the summation is over all the π electrons.

2. CHARGE DENSITY

Imagine a molecule of ethylene prior to the formation of the π bond. Each carbon atom has associated with it one electron that is available for π-bond formation. Consequently, a neutral carbon atom must have an electron density of 1, and accordingly, we define the charge density q at any carbon atom to be 1.00 minus the electron density at that atom.

$$q = 1.00 - ED$$

For ethylene the charge density at each position is:

at C_1

$$q_1 = 1.00 - ED_1$$

$$= 1.00 - 1.00 = 0.00$$

at C_2

$$q_2 = 1.00 - ED_2$$

$$= 1.00 - 1.00 = 0.00$$

The usual method for describing the allyl carbonium ion is to consider it as a resonance hybrid of the following two structures:

$$C{=}C{-}\overset{+}{C} \longleftrightarrow \overset{+}{C}{-}C{=}C$$

This requires that one half of the positive charge reside at each of the terminal positions and that the middle carbon atom be neutral. Molecular-orbital theory gives exactly the same result. The charge density at carbon atoms 1, 2, and 3 is calculated to be

$$q_1 = 1.00 - 0.500 = 0.500$$

$$q_2 = 1.00 - 1.00 \ = 0.00$$

$$q_3 = 1.00 - 0.500 = 0.500$$

In the case of the allyl radical we find for the charge density at each position:

$$q_1 = 1.00 - 1.00 = 0.00$$

$$q_2 = 1.00 - 1.00 = 0.00$$

$$q_3 = 1.00 - 1.00 = 0.00$$

In the allyl radical, the third π-electron is put into ψ_2 causing a change in electron density equal to 0.500 at carbon atoms 1 and 3, but no change at carbon atom 2. This result concurs with resonance theory which also predicts that this electron will be found at both terminal positions. The situation is similar for the allyl carbanion. The minus charge is spread out so that one half of it resides at C_1 and the other half at C_3.

$$q_1 = 1.00 - 1.50 = -0.500$$

$$q_2 = 1.00 - 1.00 = \ \ \ 0.00$$

$$q_3 = 1.00 - 1.50 = -0.500$$

The charge density in the cyclopropenyl cation is spread equally over all three positions.

$$q_1 = 1 - \tfrac{2}{3} = \tfrac{1}{3}$$

$$q_2 = 1 - \tfrac{2}{3} = \tfrac{1}{3}$$

$$q_3 = 1 - \tfrac{2}{3} = \tfrac{1}{3}$$

For the cyclopropenyl anion we find

$$q_1 = 1 - 1\frac{1}{3} = -\frac{1}{3}$$

$$q_2 = 1 - 1\frac{1}{3} = -\frac{1}{3}$$

$$q_3 = 1 - 1\frac{1}{3} = -\frac{1}{3}$$

and for butadiene and benzene the charge density is zero at all positions.

Butadiene $\quad q_1 = q_2 = q_3 = q_4 = 0.000$

Benzene $\quad q_1 = q_2 = q_3 = q_4 = q_5 = q_6 = 0.000$

3. BOND ORDER

3.1. One of the major tasks of the chemist is to correlate structure and reactivity, to explain the behavior of a molecule on the basis of chemical composition. Saturated organic hydrocarbons behave differently from unsaturated ones, the latter being far more reactive to a great variety of reagents. The site of reactivity is the olefinic linkage, and so it is natural to attempt to correlate the behavior of such compounds with the type and amount of unsaturation they contain. One possibility is to consider the number of electrons contained in a bond as a measure of the type and amount of bonding. A carbon-carbon single bond as in ethane is composed of two electrons and has a length of 1.54 A while the double-bond distance in ethylene is 1.33 A. There are four electrons in this bond. The procedure is straightforward for these simple substances, but the situation is not so clear for the more complicated molecules like butadiene and benzene. How much double-bond character is there in the various carbon-carbon linkages of these compounds? In these cases it would seem that an obvious indication comes from the interatomic distances; the greater the degree of unsaturation, the shorter the carbon-carbon bond length. However, this empirical procedure is not so straightforward as it appears. Caution must be exercised in any correlation of bond distance with the degree of unsaturation, for the bond length also depends upon the hybridization of the carbon atoms involved. An sp^2—sp^2 σ bond is shorter than an sp^3—sp^3 carbon-carbon σ bond. Increasing the amount of s character in a hybrid orbital shortens it.[1]

[1] M. J. S. Dewar, *Hyperconjugation*, Ronald Press, New York, 1962, p. 48ff.

Provided proper adjustment is made for the hybridization of the atoms involved, the bond distance is a measure of the amount of unsaturation present in a bond.

From a theoretical viewpoint, the degree of bonding between two carbon atoms (A and B) is given by the bond order p_{AB}. This was defined by Coulson in 1939 as

$$p_{AB} = \sum a_A a_B$$

the summation being over all the π electrons.[2] The procedure is similar to that employed in calculating electron densities. The amount of bonding between two carbon atoms C_A and C_B due to one electron in a given molecular orbital is equal to the product of the coefficients $a_A a_B$ for that orbital.

3.2. ETHYLENE For the double bond in ethylene, the bond order due to one π-electron is:

$$a_1 a_2 = \left(\frac{1}{\sqrt{2}}\right)\left(\frac{1}{\sqrt{2}}\right)$$

$$= \frac{1}{2}$$

There are two electrons in this bond, and the total π-bond order between the carbon atoms due to both of them is:

$$p_{12} = 2(\tfrac{1}{2}) = 1.00$$

If one includes the σ bond that also connects the atoms, the total degree of bonding between the atoms is equal to 2.00. The double bond in ethylene is a true double bond.

3.3. THE ALLYL SYSTEM In the allyl system the π-bond order between carbon atoms 1 and 2 is identical to that between carbon atoms 2 and 3. For the carbonium ion we have

$$p_{12} = p_{23} = 2\left(\frac{1}{2}\right)\left(\frac{\sqrt{2}}{2}\right) = 0.707$$

---

[2] C. A. Coulson, *Proc. Roy. Soc.*, **A 169,** 413 (1939).

The radical has two electrons in ψ_1 and one in ψ_2, and the π-bond order for the radical is:

$$p_{12} = 2\left(\frac{1}{2}\right)\left(\frac{\sqrt{2}}{2}\right) + \left(\frac{1}{\sqrt{2}}\right)(0) = 0.707$$

$$p_{23} = 2\left(\frac{\sqrt{2}}{2}\right)\left(\frac{1}{2}\right) + (0)\left(\frac{-1}{\sqrt{2}}\right) = 0.707$$

The same value is found for the carbanion.

$$p_{12} = 2\left(\frac{1}{2}\right)\left(\frac{\sqrt{2}}{2}\right) + 2\left(\frac{1}{\sqrt{2}}\right)(0) = 0.707$$

$$p_{23} = 2\left(\frac{\sqrt{2}}{2}\right)\left(\frac{1}{2}\right) + 2(0)\left(\frac{-1}{\sqrt{2}}\right) = 0.707$$

Upon inclusion of the σ bonds, the total degree of bonding between the carbon atoms is calculated to be 1.71.

3.4. BUTADIENE   Butadiene has two electrons in ψ_1 and two in ψ_2. This yields the following values for the π-bond order between adjacent carbon atoms:

$$p_{12} = 2(0.372)(0.602) + 2(0.602)(0.372) \qquad = 0.896$$

$$p_{23} = 2(0.602)(0.602) + 2(0.372)(-0.372) \quad = 0.448$$

$$p_{34} = 2(0.602)(0.372) + 2(-0.372)(-0.602) = 0.896$$

The double bonds in butadiene have some single-bond character. The total bond order for these linkages is less than 2.00 while the single bond has appreciable double-bond character. The terminal bonds in butadiene are somewhat longer than the usual olefinic distance, which agrees with our calculated result.

3.5. TRIMETHYLENEMETHANE   A calculation of the π-bond order for this species gives a value of $1/\sqrt{3}$ to each bond. There are two electrons in ψ_1, one in ψ_2, and one in ψ_3.

$$p_{14} = 2\left(\frac{1}{\sqrt{6}}\right)\left(\frac{\sqrt{3}}{\sqrt{6}}\right) + \left(\frac{1}{\sqrt{2}}\right)(0) + \left(\frac{1}{\sqrt{6}}\right)(0) = \frac{1}{\sqrt{3}}$$

$$p_{24} = 2\left(\frac{1}{\sqrt{6}}\right)\left(\frac{\sqrt{3}}{\sqrt{6}}\right) + (0)(0) + \left(\frac{-2}{\sqrt{6}}\right)(0) = \frac{1}{\sqrt{3}}$$

$$p_{34} = 2\left(\frac{1}{\sqrt{6}}\right)\left(\frac{\sqrt{3}}{\sqrt{6}}\right) + \left(\frac{-1}{\sqrt{2}}\right)(0) + \left(\frac{1}{\sqrt{6}}\right)(0) = \frac{1}{\sqrt{3}}$$

3.6. BENZENE The bond order is the same between all of the six carbon atoms in benzene. Its value being less than 2.00 implies that the bonds joining these atoms are not true double bonds. This result is expected.

$$p_{12} = 2\left(\frac{1}{\sqrt{6}}\right)\left(\frac{1}{\sqrt{6}}\right) + 2\left(\frac{1}{2}\right)\left(\frac{1}{2}\right) + 2\left(\frac{1}{\sqrt{12}}\right)\left(\frac{-1}{\sqrt{12}}\right) = \frac{2}{3}$$

$$p_{23} = 2\left(\frac{1}{\sqrt{6}}\right)\left(\frac{1}{\sqrt{6}}\right) + 2\left(\frac{1}{2}\right)(0) + 2\left(\frac{-1}{\sqrt{12}}\right)\left(\frac{-2}{\sqrt{12}}\right) = \frac{2}{3}$$

$$p_{34} = 2\left(\frac{1}{\sqrt{6}}\right)\left(\frac{1}{\sqrt{6}}\right) + 2(0)\left(-\frac{1}{2}\right) + 2\left(\frac{-2}{\sqrt{12}}\right)\left(\frac{-1}{\sqrt{12}}\right) = \frac{2}{3}$$

$$p_{45} = 2\left(\frac{1}{\sqrt{6}}\right)\left(\frac{1}{\sqrt{6}}\right) + 2\left(-\frac{1}{2}\right)\left(-\frac{1}{2}\right) + 2\left(\frac{-1}{\sqrt{12}}\right)\left(\frac{1}{\sqrt{12}}\right) = \frac{2}{3}$$

$$p_{56} = 2\left(\frac{1}{\sqrt{6}}\right)\left(\frac{1}{\sqrt{6}}\right) + 2\left(-\frac{1}{2}\right)(0) + 2\left(\frac{1}{\sqrt{12}}\right)\left(\frac{2}{\sqrt{12}}\right) = \frac{2}{3}$$

$$p_{61} = 2\left(\frac{1}{\sqrt{6}}\right)\left(\frac{1}{\sqrt{6}}\right) + 2(0)\left(\frac{1}{2}\right) + 2\left(\frac{2}{\sqrt{12}}\right)\left(\frac{1}{\sqrt{12}}\right) = \frac{2}{3}$$

The total bond order between adjacent carbon atoms, including the σ bond, is calculated to be $1\frac{2}{3}$, and this agrees with the fact that the observed bond length is 1.39 A in benzene, a value intermediate between that of the usual single and double bonds.

4. FREE VALENCE

We have just discussed the concept of bond order, an idea that was proposed by Coulson to indicate the degree of π bonding between two atoms. In this manner we can establish on a theoretical basis some connection

between the structure of a compound and the degree of bonding at the various positions. In order to carry this idea a step further, Coulson[3] in 1947 was led to postulate the free valence F at a position. This quantity is a measure of the reactivity of the various positions towards attack by free radicals. Within a molecule, that position is the most reactive that has the largest free valence. The free valence at a position is defined as :[4]

$$F = 4.73 - \sum p$$

where 4.73 is the maximum bond order that a carbon atom can have and the $\sum p$ is the total bond order that it actually does have. This definition includes σ bonds which are given a bond order of 1.00.

For ethylene the free valence at carbon atom 1 is equal to that at carbon atom 2. Each atom has three σ bonds that contribute 3.00 to the total bond order and one π bond that adds another 1.00. The total bond order is 4.00 at each position, and consequently, the free valence is 0.73.

$$F_1 = F_2 = 4.73 - 4.00 = 0.73$$

The situation becomes slightly more complex for butadiene. The total bond order at a terminal position such as at C_1 equals 3.00 for the three σ-bonds plus 0.896 for the π bond to C_2.

$$\sum p = 3.90$$

The free valence at a terminal carbon atom equals:

$$F_1 = F_4 = 4.73 - 3.90 = 0.83$$

The bond order at an internal position, say C_2, is likewise equal to 3.00 for the three single bonds. To this value must be added 0.896 representing p_{12} and 0.448 for p_{23}. Carbon atom 2 is joined by partial double bonds to both C_1 and C_3.

$$\sum p = 3.00 + 0.896 + 0.448$$

$$= 4.34$$

---

[3] C. A. Coulson, *Discussions of the Faraday Soc.*, **2**, 9 (1947).
[4] For a discussion, see W. E. Moffitt, *Trans. Faraday Soc.*, **45**, 373 (1949).

and

$$F_2 = F_3 = 4.73 - 4.34$$

$$= 0.39$$

Notice that the free valence is larger at a terminal position than at an internal carbon atom. With some reservation we may use this result to explain terminal attack of butadiene, the higher free valence indicating the greater reactivity of these carbon atoms. We must bear in mind that reactivity (the rate of a reaction) actually depends upon the free energy of activation, whereas the concept of free valence is usually employed only in connection with the reactant.

In trimethylenemethane we obtain the same value for the free valence at carbon atoms 1, 2, and 3.

$$F_1 = F_2 = F_3 = 4.73 - 3.58 = 1.15$$

The free valence at carbon atom 4, which is linked by partial double bonds to all other positions, is

$$F_4 = 4.73 - 4.73 = 0.00$$

Since all six positions in benzene are equivalent, the value of F is the same for each one. Each carbon atom is joined to two others by partial double bonds and to a hydrogen atom by a σ bond. We calculate the free valence for carbon atom 1. The total π-bond order at C_1 equals $p_{12} + p_{61}$ (1.33). To this value must be added the σ-bond order, 3.00.

$$\sum p = 4.33$$

and

$$F_1 = 4.73 - 4.33$$

$$= 0.40$$

PROBLEMS

1. Calculate the electron density, charge density, bond order, and free valence at each position in the cyclopentadienyl radical and anion.
2. Calculate the electron density, charge density, bond order, and free valence for the cyclopropenyl carbanion. First, carry out this calcula-

tion using ψ_1, ψ_2, and ψ_3 as given in section 4, Chapter 4, then repeat using ψ_1, ψ_A, and ψ_B which are given in section 12, Chapter 4. Compare the results.

3. Calculate the electron density, charge density, bond order, and free valence for each of the following systems (see Chapter 4, problem 6).

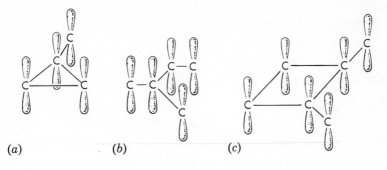

(a)   (b)   (c)

Chapter Six

HETEROCYCLIC MOLECULES

1. THE PARAMETERS, α_N AND α_O

In principle, extension of the Hückel molecular-orbital method to heterocyclic systems is straightforward. The calculations are carried out in a manner identical to that presented in Chapter 3, but the introduction of a heteroatom into the system does necessitate some change. For instance, in Chapter 3, section 3, we defined the Coulomb integral H_{AA} or α, as the energy of an electron in the $2p_z$ atomic orbital of carbon (see equation 3.1). Due to the increased electronegativity of nitrogen and oxygen, terms like α_N and α_O, which represent the energy of an electron in a $2p_z$ orbital of one of these atoms, differ from this value. An electron in such an orbital is more stable; its energy is more negative than an electron associated with a similar orbital of carbon. We must correct for this enhanced stability. Furthermore, a heteroatom is capable of donating either one or two electrons to the π-electronic system, for example, the oxygen atom in phenol donates two electrons while a carbonyl oxygen atom contributes but one. In addition we should distinguish between the donation of two electrons by phenol and the donation of two by the phenolate anion. Electronic delocalization in the former involves charge separation, making the process less favorable. As a result of these factors the values assigned to the parameters, α_N and α_O, depend upon the system under consideration, the assumptions made, and the method of evaluation[1].

The resonance integral, β, was defined as the energy of an electron when it is between two carbon atoms. In a heterocyclic system if one of the two

---

[1] For a comprehensive discussion concerning the effect of heteroatoms on molecular orbital calculations, see A. Streitwieser, Jr., *Molecular Orbital Theory for Organic Chemists*, Wiley, New York, 1961, p. 117ff.

atoms in question happens to be a nitrogen or oxygen atom, the energy of the electron decreases. The electron in a carbon-nitrogen bond is more stable than the electron in a carbon-carbon bond, and the corresponding value of β should be adjusted. We shall neglect this correction.

Wheland and Pauling[2] in their treatment of heterocyclic molecules adjusted the values of α_N and α_O by expressing them in terms of α plus some multiple of β.

$$\alpha_N = \alpha + \lambda_N\beta$$

$$\alpha_O = \alpha + \lambda_O\beta$$

where λ is a number, in this case positive, which is chosen so that α_N and α_O have the desired values. Reasonable agreement with experimental data is obtained by assigning the following values to these parameters:

$$\alpha_N(1) = \alpha + \tfrac{1}{2}\beta$$

$$\alpha_N(2) = \alpha + \tfrac{3}{2}\beta$$

$$\alpha_O(1) = \alpha + \tfrac{3}{2}\beta$$

$$\alpha_O(2) = \alpha + \tfrac{5}{2}\beta$$

where $\alpha_N(1)$ and $\alpha_O(1)$ are to be used in calculations involving the donation of one electron by the respective atoms and $\alpha_N(2)$ and $\alpha_O(2)$ for those involving two electrons. The contribution of two electrons by the heteroatom decreases the shielding at that position. The electrons in the π system are under the influence of a more attractive potential, and the energy of an electron in the $2p_z$ orbital of such an atom decreases, a result that is reflected in the lowering of α. Pyridine[3] and pyrrole exemplify the two possibilities.

The π-electronic energy of many heterocyclic systems may be evaluated once the Coulomb integrals for the heteroatoms have been properly adjusted (this is not always easy). Thus, calculations involving sulfur and the halogens can also be carried out. The procedure is the same in principle for all of these, and we illustrate the concepts with pyrrole.

---

[2] G. W. Wheland and L. Pauling, *J. Am. Chem. Soc.*, **57**, 2086 (1935); G. W. Wheland, *ibid.*, **64**, 900 (1942).

[3] For a molecular orbital treatment of pyridine, including overlap, see K. B. Wiberg, *Physical Organic Chemistry*, Wiley, New York, 1964, p. 77ff; see also G. W. Wheland, *Resonance in Organic Chemistry*, Wiley, New York, 1955, p. 670ff.

2. PYRROLE

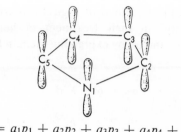

$$\psi = a_1p_1 + a_2p_2 + a_3p_3 + a_4p_4 + a_5p_5$$

where p_1 represents the $2p_z$ atomic orbital of nitrogen. The secular equation takes the usual form:

$$\begin{vmatrix} H_{11} - S_{11}E & H_{12} - S_{12}E & H_{13} - S_{13}E & H_{14} - S_{14}E & H_{15} - S_{15}E \\ H_{21} - S_{21}E & H_{22} - S_{22}E & H_{23} - S_{23}E & H_{24} - S_{24}E & H_{25} - S_{25}E \\ H_{31} - S_{31}E & H_{32} - S_{32}E & H_{33} - S_{33}E & H_{34} - S_{34}E & H_{35} - S_{35}E \\ H_{41} - S_{41}E & H_{42} - S_{42}E & H_{43} - S_{43}E & H_{44} - S_{44}E & H_{45} - S_{45}E \\ H_{51} - S_{51}E & H_{52} - S_{52}E & H_{53} - S_{53}E & H_{54} - S_{54}E & H_{55} - S_{55}E \end{vmatrix} = 0$$

Making the appropriate substitutions yields:

$$\begin{vmatrix} \alpha_N(2) - E & \beta & 0 & 0 & \beta \\ \beta & \alpha - E & \beta & 0 & 0 \\ 0 & \beta & \alpha - E & \beta & 0 \\ 0 & 0 & \beta & \alpha - E & \beta \\ \beta & 0 & 0 & \beta & \alpha - E \end{vmatrix} = 0$$

Replacing $\alpha_N(2)$ by $(\alpha + \frac{3}{2}\beta)$,

$$\begin{vmatrix} \alpha + \frac{3}{2}\beta - E & \beta & 0 & 0 & \beta \\ \beta & \alpha - E & \beta & 0 & 0 \\ 0 & \beta & \alpha - E & \beta & 0 \\ 0 & 0 & \beta & \alpha - E & \beta \\ \beta & 0 & 0 & \beta & \alpha - E \end{vmatrix} = 0$$

Dividing through by β and letting $x = (\alpha - E)/\beta$, we obtain:

$$\begin{vmatrix} x + \frac{3}{2} & 1 & 0 & 0 & 1 \\ 1 & x & 1 & 0 & 0 \\ 0 & 1 & x & 1 & 0 \\ 0 & 0 & 1 & x & 1 \\ 1 & 0 & 0 & 1 & x \end{vmatrix} = 0$$

To solve for x we expand the determinant.

$$(x + \tfrac{3}{2}) \cdot \begin{vmatrix} x & 1 & 0 & 0 \\ 1 & x & 1 & 0 \\ 0 & 1 & x & 1 \\ 0 & 0 & 1 & x \end{vmatrix} - 1 \cdot \begin{vmatrix} 1 & 1 & 0 & 0 \\ 0 & x & 1 & 0 \\ 0 & 1 & x & 1 \\ 1 & 0 & 1 & x \end{vmatrix} + 1 \cdot \begin{vmatrix} 1 & x & 1 & 0 \\ 0 & 1 & x & 1 \\ 0 & 0 & 1 & x \\ 1 & 0 & 0 & 1 \end{vmatrix} = 0$$

Expanding further yields the polynomial equation

$$x^5 + \tfrac{3}{2}x^4 - 5x^3 - \tfrac{9}{2}x^2 + 5x + \tfrac{7}{2} = 0$$

which has the roots, $x = -2.55$, $x = -1.15$, $x = -0.618$, $x = 1.20$, $x = 1.62$.

$$x = -2.55$$
$$E_1 = \alpha + 2.55\beta$$

$$x = -1.15$$
$$E_2 = \alpha + 1.15\beta$$

$$x = -0.618$$
$$E_3 = \alpha + 0.618\beta$$

$$x = 1.20$$
$$E_4 = \alpha - 1.20\beta$$

$$x = 1.62$$
$$E_5 = \alpha - 1.62\beta$$

FIGURE 6–1 THE PYRROLE MOLE-
CULE WITH LOCALIZED π ELECTRONS

The classical structure has two electrons on the nitrogen atom that con-
tribute $2(\alpha + \tfrac{3}{2} \beta)$ or $2\alpha + 3.00\beta$ to the energy of the π system. The
resonance energy is calculated to be

$$\text{resonance energy} = 6\alpha + 7.00\beta - (6\alpha + 8.64\beta)$$

$$= -1.64\beta$$

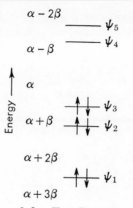

FIGURE 6–2   THE ENERGY OF
THE π ELECTRONS IN PYRROLE

From the secular equation we are able to obtain the homogeneous equations, which when written in terms of x become:

$$a_1(x + \tfrac{3}{2}) + a_2 \qquad\qquad\qquad + a_5 = 0$$
$$a_1 \qquad + a_2 x + a_3 \qquad\qquad = 0$$
$$a_2 + a_3 x + a_4 \qquad = 0$$
$$a_3 + a_4 x + a_5 = 0$$
$$a_1 \qquad\qquad\qquad + a_4 + a_5 x = 0$$

The coefficients a_1 through a_5 for each molecular orbital are found using the technique given in Chapter 4. We substitute the appropriate value of x into the homogeneous equations and determine the coefficients corresponding to that x. The normalization requirement remains unaltered.

$$\int \psi_A \psi_A = 1$$

and
$$a_1{}^2 + a_2{}^2 + a_3{}^2 + a_4{}^2 + a_5{}^2 = 1$$

In this manner we obtain the five normalized eigenfunctions for pyrrole.

$$\psi_1 = 0.749 p_1 + 0.393 p_2 + 0.254 p_3 + 0.254 p_4 + 0.393 p_5$$
$$\psi_2 = 0.503 p_1 - 0.089 p_2 - 0.605 p_3 - 0.605 p_4 - 0.089 p_5$$
$$\psi_3 = 0.602 p_2 + 0.372 p_3 - 0.372 p_4 - 0.602 p_5$$
$$\psi_4 = 0.430 p_1 - 0.580 p_2 + 0.267 p_3 + 0.267 p_4 - 0.580 p_5$$
$$\psi_5 = 0.372 p_2 - 0.602 p_3 + 0.602 p_4 - 0.372 p_5$$

There is a convenient way of checking whether the coefficients that we find for any given molecular orbital are correct, and we demonstrate this technique using ψ_1. The energy of ψ_1 was given as $\alpha + 2.55\beta$. Now, according to the Schrödinger equation, the energy of ψ_1 is

$$H\psi_1 = E\psi_1$$

where E must equal $\alpha + 2.55\beta$. Let us multiply both sides of this equation by ψ_1 and integrate.

$$\int \psi_1 H\psi_1 \, dv = \int \psi_1 E\psi_1 \, dv$$

Solving for E,

$$E = \frac{\int \psi_1 H\psi_1 \, dv}{\int \psi_1 \psi_1 \, dv}$$

Since our eigenfunctions are normalized,

$$\int \psi_1 \psi_1 \, dv = 1$$

and

$$E = \int \psi_1 H\psi_1 \, dv \qquad (6.1)$$

This integral must have a value of $\alpha + 2.55\beta$. Let us see if it does. Substituting for ψ_1 into this equation,

$$\psi_1 = 0.749p_1 + 0.393p_2 + 0.254p_3 + 0.254p_4 + 0.393p_5$$

Remember that $H_{AB} = H_{BA}$ (see Chapter 3, section 5); then,

$$
\begin{aligned}
E = {} & (0.749)^2 H_{11} + (0.393)^2 H_{22} + (0.254)^2 H_{33} + (0.254)^2 H_{44} + (0.393)^2 H_{55} \\
& + 2(0.749)(0.393)H_{12} + 2(0.393)(0.254)H_{23} + 2(0.254)(0.254)H_{34} \\
& + 2(0.254)(0.393)H_{45} + 2(0.749)(0.393)H_{15} \\
& + \text{other terms that have zero value } (H_{13}, H_{14}, \text{ and so forth})
\end{aligned}
$$

Since $H_{11} = \alpha + \frac{3}{2}\beta$, substitution of the parameters, α and β, into the above expression leads to:

$$E = (0.749)^2(\alpha + \tfrac{3}{2}\beta) + 2(0.393)^2(\alpha) + 2(0.254)^2(\alpha)$$
$$+ 4(0.294)(\beta) + 4(0.100)(\beta) + 2(0.065)(\beta)$$

$$E = \alpha + 0.842\beta + 1.18\beta + 0.400\beta + 0.130\beta$$

$$E = \alpha + 2.55\beta$$

That the eigenvalue is correct confirms the values assigned to the coefficients. This technique is perfectly general, and the energy of any normalized molecular orbital is given by equation (6.1).

Returning to pyrrole, we calculate next the electron density at each position. There are two electrons in each of the bonding molecular orbitals.

$$ED_1 = 2(0.749)^2 + 2(0.503)^2 \qquad\qquad = 1.63$$

$$ED_2 = 2(0.393)^2 + 2(-0.089)^2 + 2(0.602)^2 \quad = 1.05$$

$$ED_3 = 2(0.254)^2 + 2(-0.605)^2 + 2(0.372)^2 \quad = 1.14$$

$$ED_4 = 2(0.254)^2 + 2(-0.605)^2 + 2(-0.372)^2 = 1.14$$

$$ED_5 = 2(0.393)^2 + 2(-0.089)^2 + 2(-0.602)^2 = 1.05$$

The electron density at every position is greater than unity. Since six electrons are spread over only five atoms, this result is not surprising.

To calculate the charge density, we take notice of the fact that a neutral nitrogen atom in pyrrole ought to have two electrons associated with it. Thus, the charge density at the nitrogen atom is defined as:

$$q_1 = 2.00 - ED_1$$

and the charge density at each of the various positions is:

$$q_1 = 2.00 - 1.63 = \quad 0.37$$

$$q_2 = 1.00 - 1.05 = -0.05$$

$$q_3 = 1.00 - 1.14 = -0.14$$

$$q_4 = 1.00 - 1.14 = -0.14$$

$$q_5 = 1.00 - 1.05 = -0.05$$

The bond order between any two adjacent atoms is calculated in the manner described previously, as is the free valence. In general, a molecular-orbital calculation for a heterocyclic molecule yields a result that is in good agreement with experimental observations. This is due to the empirical evaluation of all parameters. Because of the reasons stated earlier, the situation is somewhat more complicated than for a hydrocarbon, and many assumptions, tacit and otherwise, have been made. It is the empirical nature of the theory that, to a large measure, corrects for these and gives rise to results that are reasonably accurate.

PROBLEMS

1. Carry out a complete Hückel molecular-orbital calculation on the carbonyl system. Include electron densities, charge densities, and so forth. The charge density on the oxygen atom is 1.00 minus the electron density since the oxygen contributes only one electron to the π system.

$$q_O = 1.00 - ED_O$$

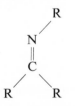

2. Carry out a complete calculation, including determination of the coefficients, bond orders, and so forth, on the Schiff base — remember that the nitrogen atom contributes only one π-electron to the system.

$$
\begin{array}{c}
R \\
\diagup \\
N \\
\parallel \\
C \\
\diagup \quad \diagdown \\
R \qquad R
\end{array}
$$

3. Calculate the excitation energies for the two compounds presented in problems 1 and 2.
4. Calculate the resonance energy of the anion of acetaldehyde.

$$\overset{\delta^-}{CH_2} = CH = \overset{\delta^-}{O}$$

5. Find the resonance energy of acrolein.

$$CH_2 = CH - CH = O$$

6. Recalculate the π-electronic energy levels of the compounds given in problems 1 and 2. Include overlap in the calculation. Use 0.25 for the value of the overlap integral.

7. Confirm that the coefficients given for ψ_3 for pyrrole are correct.

Chapter Seven

THE CONCEPT OF AROMATICITY

1. THE STRUCTURE OF BENZENE[1]

Organic compounds are divided into two categories, the *aliphatic* and the *aromatic* series. These divisions were made years ago when little was known concerning structure and reactivity, and substances were classified according to some simple physical characteristic (fatlike or fragrant). This older criterion is no longer applicable, yet the terminology remains.

In 1825, Faraday isolated benzene as a constituent of the oil that collected in illuminating-gas lines. Nine years later Mitscherlich obtained the same compound from the dry distillation of benzoic acid with lime. He named the compound benzin because of its relation to benzoic acid and benzoin. Subsequently, this name was changed to benzol in the German literature and to benzene in the French and English literature.

By 1865, the concept of valency had been sufficiently well formulated to explain the structures and reactivity of aliphatic compounds, and in order to fit the structure of benzene within this framework, Kekulé[2] proposed that it was a cyclic compound containing six carbon atoms with alternating double and single bonds.

This idea was modified in 1872. The number of isomers of a disubstituted benzene obtained experimentally did not agree with this structure, and that

---

[1] For a review of the history of benzene see C. K. Ingold, *Structure and Mechanism in Organic Chemistry*, Cornell University Press, Ithaca, N.Y., 1953, p. 156ff.
[2] F. A. Kekulé, *Bull. Soc. Chim.*, France, **3**, 98 (1865); F. A. Kekulé, *Ann.*, **137**, 129 (1866).

year Kekulé postulated that the single and double bonds in benzene were not static at all but existed in a state of rapid oscillation.[3]

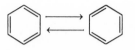

At about the same time (1867) Dewar proposed his bicyclic structure.[4]

Later, when Ladenburg demonstrated the equivalence of the six positions in benzene,[5] this structure had to be discarded.

In 1869 Ladenburg proposed his own prism formula.[6]

This formula solves the problem concerning the function of the fourth valence of carbon, the puzzling feature in other structures. However, Baeyer demonstrated unequivocally that this formula could not be correct. For a given pair of substituents only one ortho disubstituted benzene exists and Ladenburg argued that these compounds had the following geometry:

Baeyer showed that ortho substituents occupied adjacent carbon atoms.[7] This plus lack of optical activity in the disubstituted benzenes was sufficient. The prism structure was discarded.

The difficulty lay in the fourth valence of each carbon atom — how to account for this — Claus proposed his diagonal structure where the fourth valence of each carbon atom was used in the formation of a *para* bond.[8]

[3] F. A. Kekulé, *Ann.*, **162,** 77 (1872).
[4] J. Dewar, *Proc. Roy. Soc. Edinburgh*, **6,** 82 (1867).
[5] A. Ladenburg, *Ber.*, **7,** 1684 (1874).
[6] A. Ladenburg, *Ber.*, **2,** 140 (1869).
[7] A. v. Baeyer, *Ber.*, **23,** 1272 (1890).
[8] A. Claus, *Ber.*, **15,** 1405 (1882).

In its final form, his idea was that these diagonal bonds did not represent the usual type of chemical bond, but rather that they merely symbolized in some way the fourth valence of carbon. This same idea was set forth in the centric structure of Armstrong[9] and Baeyer.[10]

Although this proposal suffers from the same inadequacy as the previous one, that is, the nature of the centric bonds is not clear, it was employed quite successfully by Bamberger[11] to explain the properties of aromatic compounds. He stated that each carbon atom had one valence (affinity) directed toward the center of the ring, and that these six affinities were responsible for the stability and behavior of aromatic systems. Pyridine was aromatic and yet basic because two affinities remained for bond formation while pyrrole was not basic because all affinities were used for the centric bonds.

These ideas are not so different from our present concepts.

Thiele's idea concerning the structure of benzene was put forth in 1899.[12] His theory of partial valence had answered satisfactorily the question of terminal addition to conjugated olefins, and he sought to extend these concepts to benzene. According to Thiele, in a system of alternating double and single bonds, part of the double-bond character is spread out onto the intervening single bonds while the terminal positions of the system are left with free valence and reactivity. This is illustrated for 1,3-butadiene:

$$\overset{\cdots}{C}{=}C{\cdots}C{=}\overset{\cdots}{C}$$

In 1,3-butadiene prior to double-bond formation, the fourth valence of each carbon atom is available for bond formation. Part of this valence is used to form the usual double bonds. In addition, the central carbon atoms

[9] H. E. Armstrong, *J. Chem. Soc.*, **51**, 258 (1887).

[10] A. v. Baeyer, *Ann.*, **245**, 103 (1888).

[11] E. Bamberger, *Ber.*, **24**, 1758 (1891); E. Bamberger, *Ann.*, **273**, 373 (1893).

[12] J. Thiele, *Ann.*, **306**, 87 (1899).

use the remainder of their valence to form a partial double bond between them. This leaves unused valence for potential reaction at the terminal positions.

In applying these ideas to benzene, Thiele started with a Kekulé structure and allowed the double-bond character to spread out onto the single bonds until all six positions were equivalent.

There being no terminal positions in the cyclic compound, Thiele argued that no free valence remained and therefore, little reactivity. Thiele's structure not only gives the correct isomer number for substituted benzenes; it also explains the stability of benzene. The theory is strikingly similar to the idea of orbital overlap, but remember that this hypothesis was proposed some twenty-five years before the development of quantum mechanics and seventeen years before the theory of the covalent bond. At that time the concept of partial valence was vague, and Thiele was unable to describe the term explicitly.

Later, with the development of the electronic theory of bonding, the concept of valence could be expressed more definitively, and thus the advent of electronic theory caused rapid advancement. In terms of this theory those systems were especially stable that possessed an aromatic sextet (see Figure 7–1).[13] Six electrons imparted aromaticity to a cyclic compound. Using this criterion, benzene, pyrrole, pyridine, and cyclopentadienyl carbanion were aromatic, whereas cyclobutadiene and cyclooctatetraene were not.

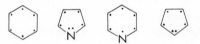

Compounds possessing an aromatic sextet

Nonaromatic compounds

FIGURE 7–1

Simultaneously, the electronic theory of mesomerism was developed by Ingold,[14] and the two were brought together by quantum mechanics. A

---

[13] J. W. Armit and R. Robinson, *J. Chem. Soc.*, **127**, 1604 (1925).

mesomeric description of benzene demonstrates the similarity between Kekulé's structures and Thiele's idea of partial valence, and stability is thought to stem from electronic delocalization.[15]

The explicit application of quantum mechanics to the structure of benzene may be formulated using either of two approximations. A molecular-orbital approach to the problem has already been discussed, and in the next section we mention briefly the valence-bond method.

2. THE VALENCE-BOND TREATMENT OF BENZENE

The first example of what is called today the valence-bond approach was presented by Heitler and London in their calculation of the energy of the hydrogen molecule.[16] In the early 1930's, Slater[17] and Pauling[18] made major contributions to the theory, extending the concepts, and applying them to organic molecules, and in fact, the valence-bond method is often called the Heitler-London-Slater-Pauling approach. This method, more closely related to the chemists' ideas than the molecular-orbital technique, considers molecules to be composed of atoms, and bonds to arise from orbital overlap. A covalent bond contains two electrons of opposite spin. The properties of molecules can be expressed in terms of the behavior of the constituent atoms and the bonds that bind them.

According to this theory, a molecule cannot be represented adequately by any one valence-bond (classical) structure, several structures being necessary to describe the molecule accurately. The substance is then said to be a resonance hybrid receiving contributions from these classical structures, and the energy of the hybrid is lower than the energy of any of the contributors.

There are certain requirements that must be met by the contributors in order that they may be considered acceptable. The number of unpaired electrons must be the same in all structures. Thus, the hydrogen chloride molecule may be considered as a resonance hybrid of I and II since neither

---

[14] C. K. Ingold and E. H. Ingold, *J. Chem. Soc.*, 1310 (1926).

[15] C. K. Ingold, *Structure and Mechanism in Organic Chemistry*, Cornell University Press, Ithaca, N.Y., 1953, p. 82.

[16] W. Heitler and F. London, *Z. Physik*, **44**, 455 (1927).

[17] J. C. Slater, *Phys. Rev.*, **38**, 1109 (1931).

[18] L. Pauling, *J. Chem. Phys.*, **1**, 280 (1933).

has any unpaired electrons, but structure III cannot contribute to the ground state since it has two unpaired electrons.

$$\text{H—Cl} \qquad \text{H}^+ :\text{Cl}^- \qquad \text{H}\cdot\ \cdot\text{Cl}$$

$$\text{I} \qquad\qquad \text{II} \qquad\qquad \text{III}$$

Secondly the electrons and the nuclei must occupy almost the same positions in all resonance contributors. This excludes the possibility of considering isomers as resonance contributors. Finally, if resonance between the structures is to be large, the energy of each of the various contributing structures should be about the same. High energy structures contribute little to the hybrid. If these conditions are fulfilled, then resonance will exist between the possible valence-bond structures. The application of these ideas to the structure and stability of benzene was first reported by Hückel[19] and somewhat later by Pauling and Wheland[20] who modified the treatment.

Valence-bond calculations are also carried out in terms of two parameters, Q and J. The first of these parameters, Q, is the Coulomb integral for the problem while the second, J, is called the exchange integral. Resonance energies are expressed in terms of the latter. Assuming benzene (IV) to be a resonance hybrid of the two Kekulé structures A and B (all bond distances are equal to 1.39 A), we are looking for the resonance energy of the benzene molecule.

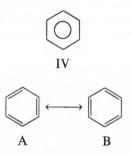

IV

A   B

One makes the usual assumption that no interaction occurs between σ and π electrons, and that in going from a Kekulé structure to benzene the σ-bond framework undergoes no change. Therefore, the energy difference between one of the Kekulé structures and the actual benzene molecule (IV) is a function of the six π-electrons only. This is the vertical resonance energy (see Figure 3–5). Let us describe the six π-electrons in Kekulé structure A

[19] E. Hückel, *Z. Physik*, **70,** 204 (1931).
[20] L. Pauling and G. W. Wheland, *J. Chem. Phys.*, **1,** 362 (1933).

by the eigenfunction ψ_A and those in structure B by ψ_B. Notice that here we have six-electron eigenfunctions as compared to the one-electron eigenfunctions encountered in the Hückel theory. Since benzene is a resonance hybrid of A and B, the eigenfunction ψ describing the π electrons in IV may be represented as a linear combination of ψ_A and ψ_B.

$$\psi = a_1\psi_A + a_2\psi_B \tag{7.1}$$

The energy of the electrons represented by this eigenfunction is given by the Schrödinger equation.

$$H\psi = E\psi$$

Substituting for ψ its equivalent as given by equation (7.1):

$$H(a_1\psi_A + a_2\psi_B) = E(a_1\psi_A + a_2\psi_B) \tag{7.2}$$

Again we are looking for the values of a_1 and a_2 that minimize the energy of the system. This is similar to the problem discussed in Chapter 3, section 5, and one employs the same variational procedure. Multiplying both sides of equation (7.2) by ψ, integrating (the integrations here involve six-electron eigenfunctions) and solving for E, we obtain

$$E = \frac{\int (a_1\psi_A + a_2\psi_B)H(a_1\psi_A + a_2\psi_B)\,dv}{\int (a_1\psi_A + a_2\psi_B)(a_1\psi_A + a_2\psi_B)\,dv}$$

Working through, we obtain two homogeneous linear equations, identical in form to expression (3.16).

$$a_1(H_{AA} - S_{AA}E) + a_2(H_{AB} - S_{AB}E) = 0$$

$$a_1(H_{BA} - S_{BA}E) + a_2(H_{BB} - S_{BB}E) = 0$$

where

$$H_{AA} = \int \psi_A H\psi_A\,dv$$

and

$$H_{AB} = \int \psi_A H\psi_B\,dv, \text{ and so forth}$$

and from the homogeneous equations, the secular equation,

$$\begin{vmatrix} H_{AA} - S_{AA}E & H_{AB} - S_{AB}E \\ H_{BA} - S_{BA}E & H_{BB} - S_{BB}E \end{vmatrix} = 0$$

Development of this determinant in terms of the two parameters and solving the expression for E yields the result:[21]

$$E = Q + 2.4J$$

where E is the energy of the six π-electrons.

In order to determine the resonance energy of benzene, we must know the π-electronic energy of a Kekulé structure (A or B). This equals the Coulomb integral Q, plus one exchange integral J for each π bond, minus a term $0.5J$ for adjacent carbon atoms not joined by a π bond. In structure A there are three π bonds and three pairs of adjacent atoms not connected by π bonds. The energy of this system is

$$E_A = Q + 3.0J - 1.5J$$

$$E_A = Q + 1.5J$$

and the resonance energy of benzene from this calculation equals:

$$\text{resonance energy} = Q + 1.5J - (Q + 2.4J)$$

$$\text{resonance energy} = -0.9J$$

A more refined calculation of the resonance energy includes not only the Kekulé structures but also the three Dewar structures, and benzene is considered to be a hybrid of the five resonance contributors ($A - E$).

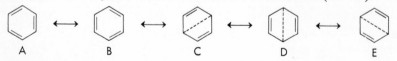

A   B   C   D   E

The eigenfunction for this treatment takes into account all five contributors.

$$\psi = a_1\psi_A + a_2\psi_B + a_3\psi_C + a_4\psi_D + a_5\psi_E$$

---

[21] For a complete valence-bond calculation, see G. W. Wheland, *Resonance in Organic Chemistry*, Wiley, New York, 1955, p. 629ff.

The secular equation becomes

$$\begin{vmatrix} H_{AA}-S_{AA}E & H_{AB}-S_{AB}E & H_{AC}-S_{AC}E & H_{AD}-S_{AD}E & H_{AE}-S_{AE}E \\ H_{BA}-S_{BA}E & H_{BB}-S_{BB}E & H_{BC}-S_{BC}E & H_{BD}-S_{BD}E & H_{BE}-S_{BE}E \\ H_{CA}-S_{CA}E & H_{CB}-S_{CB}E & H_{CC}-S_{CC}E & H_{CD}-S_{CD}E & H_{CE}-S_{CE}E \\ H_{DA}-S_{DA}E & H_{DB}-S_{DB}E & H_{DC}-S_{DC}E & H_{DD}-S_{DD}E & H_{DE}-S_{DE}E \\ H_{EA}-S_{EA}E & H_{EB}-S_{EB}E & H_{EC}-S_{EC}E & H_{ED}-S_{ED}E & H_{EE}-S_{EE}E \end{vmatrix} = 0$$

Solving this secular equation for E, one finds that the energy of the system is now

$$E = Q + 2.6J$$

which leads to a larger value for the resonance energy.

$$\text{resonance energy} = Q + 1.5J - (Q + 2.6J)$$

$$\text{resonance energy} = -1.1J$$

The energy of benzene is calculated to be lower, and therefore, the resonance energy to be larger, the more resonance contributors one uses in the calculation. This is a general result. The use of more valence-bond contributors gives a more exact description of any molecule. Of course, this makes the calculation much more difficult.

In general, the valence-bond method gives results that are in good accord with those obtained from a molecular-orbital calculation, yet the latter technique is employed more frequently. The molecular-orbital approach gives the energy of occupied as well as unoccupied orbitals, and this permits the evaluation of excitation energies. These cannot be found as readily from the valence-bond treatment. Furthermore, the one deals with one-electron eigenfunctions and one-electron Hamiltonians while the other uses many-electron eigenfunctions and consequently many-electron Hamiltonians. Mathematical evaluation of the many-electron problem is not possible, and even accurate empirical evaluation is difficult. As a result, far more effort has been spent in the development of the molecular-orbital theory.

Valence-bond theory does not explain why certain monocyclic π-electronic systems possess stability when others display instability[22] while

---

[22] For a full discussion, see D. P. Craig, Chapter I, in *Non-Benzenoid Aromatic Compounds*, Interscience, New York, 1959, D. Ginsberg (ed.).

the molecular-orbital method gives rise to a simple rule that adequately explains this fact.

3. HÜCKEL'S RULE

As early as 1931 Hückel[23] recognized that $4n + 2$ π-electrons imparted stability to completely conjugated monocyclic systems. Here n may take on the values 0, 1, 2, 3 $\cdots$. This observation which explains in modern terms the concept of aromaticity as applied to these compounds is usually referred to as the $4n + 2$ rule or Hückel's rule. Interpreted from a molecular-orbital viewpoint, Hückel's rule implies that stability is attained when all the molecular orbitals at a given energy level are completely occupied. We may call this a closed-shell configuration. The situation is analogous to that existing in the inert gases. These materials are also chemically inert because they have stable electronic configurations. Here, all the atomic orbitals up to some fixed energy level are full.

The cyclopropenyl system has molecular orbitals at two energy levels, a bonding level of energy $\alpha + 2\beta$ containing ψ_1, and an antibonding level at $\alpha - \beta$ which is degenerate. The introduction of two π-electrons fills the bonding orbital, and the lowest energy level (shell) is now complete. This satisfies Hückel's rule ($n = 0$), and the cyclopropenyl carbonium ion is aromatic (see Figure 3–12).

In the cyclopentadienyl system there are three different energy levels. The lowest shell contains only ψ_1; the second is twofold degenerate containing ψ_2 and ψ_3 while the third is also doubly degenerate with ψ_4 and ψ_5 being found at this level. A closed-shell configuration is most easily attained by filling the three bonding orbitals. Six electrons are required. The two lowest energy levels are complete; and the system is now aromatic (see Figure 3–16).

The situation is similar for benzene. Here, four energy levels are present, for both the second and third levels are doubly degenerate. The six π-electrons of benzene completely fill the two lowest shells, and of course, benzene is aromatic.

Let us turn our attention to the case of cyclobutadiene which is a non-aromatic molecule. In terms of energy shells the second level is only half full, for ψ_2 and ψ_3 each contain only one electron. However, a closed-shell configuration is achieved upon removal of these two electrons. The cyclobutadienyl dicarbonium ion with two electrons in ψ_1 is aromatic and has a resonance energy equal to -2β. However, our molecular-orbital calculation

---

[23] E. Hückel, *Z. Physik*, **70,** 204 (1931).

neglects the Coulombic repulsion that exists in a dication of this type. This repulsion between positive charges apparently destabilizes the dicarbonium ion, for all attempts at its synthesis have been unsuccessful.[24]

As originally stated, Hückel's rule applied only to monocyclic systems such as the examples illustrated in the preceding paragraphs. Since its conception the rule has been applied to other molecules outside this realm. While this is often done without *a priori* justification the properties predicted for a molecule on this basis are usually in agreement with experimental findings. The polynuclear aromatics such as naphthalene, anthracene, and phenanthrene are said to *obey Hückel's rule.*

 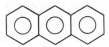

In addition, a compound such as azulene (V) is predicted to show aromatic properties on this basis.

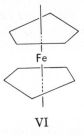

V

Some of these examples are far removed from the simple cyclic compounds discussed earlier, yet molecular-orbital calculations and of course, experimental evidence from the laboratory support the idea of aromaticity in these materials. Care must be exercised in any empirical application of the $4n + 2$ rule. The molecular-orbital criterion is a closed-shell configuration

Fe

VI

[24] H. H. Freedman and A. M. Frantz, *J. Am. Chem. Soc.*, **84**, 4165 (1962); see, however, R. F. Bryan, *J. Am. Chem. Soc.*, **86**, 733 (1964); T. J. Katz, J. R. Hall, and W. C. Neikam, *J. Am. Chem. Soc.*, **84**, 3199 (1962).

of which this rule is merely an outgrowth. Even ferrocene (VI) with eighteen available electrons is aromatic by this standard.

Remember that the Fe supplies six valence electrons to the system.

$$FeCl_2 + 2 \quad \underset{\text{H H}}{\text{(structure)}} \quad + 2R_3N \rightarrow VI + 2R_3NH^+ Cl^-$$

The ferrocene molecule has nine low energy molecular orbitals that occur at six different energy levels, three levels being doubly degenerate. The eighteen electrons that completely fill these nine orbitals give ferrocene the necessary closed-shell configuration.

There is one more point that should be brought up in connection with our discussion of aromaticity. Should a molecule be considered aromatic if vacant bonding or nonbonding orbitals are present? Naturally, the answer depends upon one's definition of aromaticity, and the question is open. For example, we have considered the cyclopropenyl carbonium ion and the cyclobutadienyl dication as aromatic. The question is academic, but how about the cyclopentadienyl trication — is it aromatic? Hückel's rule is obeyed. The system has a closed-shell configuration and is calculated to have a large resonance energy. Nevertheless, two bonding orbitals remain unoccupied, and therefore, exceptional stability is not expected. The addition of electrons to these orbitals should occur readily.

A similar situation is encountered in the case of fulvalene (VII).

VII

It obeys Hückel's rule and is calculated to have a large resonance energy, yet not all bonding molecular orbitals are full. It should add two electrons easily and thereby form a dianion, that does have all bonding orbitals completely occupied. Now which is aromatic, fulvalene or its dianion, or both?

PROBLEMS

1. Assuming that the hydrogen chloride molecule is a resonance hybrid of the following two valence-bond contributors, set up the secular equation for the system.

$$H—Cl \longleftrightarrow H^+ :Cl^-$$

2. Which of the following do you consider to be aromatic?
   (a) The cyclopentadienyl carbonium ion
   (b) The cycloheptatrienyl carbonium ion
   (c) cyclooctatetraene
   (d)

   (e) The dianion of cyclooctatetraene
   (f) The dianion of cyclobutadiene
3. Calculate the energy of the following two valence-bond structures in terms of the parameters Q and J. (Assume cyclooctatetraene to be a planar molecule.)

4. Which ionic structures may be included in a valence-bond treatment of benzene?

RECOMMENDED ADDITIONAL READING

Cartmell, E, and G. W. A. Fowles, *Valency and Molecular Structure*, Butterworth, London, 1961.

Cotton F. A. *Chemical Applications of Group Theory*, Interscience, New York and London, 1965.

Coulson, C. A. *Valence*, Oxford University Press, London, 1952.

Daudel, R., R. Lefebvre, and C. Moser. *Quantum Chemistry*, Interscience, New York, 1959.

Dewar, M. J. S. *An Introduction to Modern Chemistry*, Oxford, New York, 1965.

Gray, H. B. *Electrons and Chemical Bonding*, W. A. Benjamin, Inc., New York, 1964.

Jaffé, H. H., and M. Orchin. *Symmetry in Chemistry*, Wiley, New York, 1965.

Karagounis, G. *Introductory Organic Quantum Chemistry*, Academic Press, Inc., New York and London, 1962.

King, G. W. *Spectroscopy and Molecular Structure*, Holt, Rinehart and Winston, Inc., New York, 1964.

Linnett, W. L. *Wave Mechanics and Valency*, Methuen & Co., Ltd., London, 1960.

Pauling, L. *Nature of the Chemical Bond*, 3d ed., Cornell University Press, Ithaca, New York, 1960.

Pullman, A., and B. Pullman. *Les Théories Electroniques de la Chimie Organique*, Masson et Cie., Paris, 1952.

Pullman, B. *The Modern Theory of Molecular Structure*, Dover, New York, 1962.

Roberts, J. D. *Notes on Molecular Orbital Calculations*, W. A. Benjamin, Inc., New York, 1961.

Sherwin, C. W. *Introduction to Quantum Mechanics*, Holt, Rinehart and Winston, Inc., New York, 1959.

Simpson, W. T. *Theories of Electrons in Molecules*, Prentice-Hall, Englewood Cliffs, N. J., 1962.

Streitwieser, A. Jr. *Molecular Orbital Theory for Organic Chemists*, Wiley, New York, 1961.

Syrkin, L. K., and M. E. Dyatkina, *Structure of Molecules and the Chemical Bond*, Butterworth, London, 1950.

Wheland, G. W. *Resonance in Organic Chemistry*, Wiley, New York, 1955.

Wiberg, K. B. *Physical Organic Chemistry*, Wiley, New York, 1964.

AUTHOR INDEX

SUBJECT INDEX